THE GOLD'S GYM WEIGHT TRAINING BOOK

Building a Beautiful,
Strong & Healthy Body

THE GOLD'S GYM WEIGHT TRAINING BOOK

Bill Dobbins & Ken Sprague

Photography by Carol Vitz & Michael Wilder

Illustration by Matt Golden

 **J. P. Tarcher, Inc.**
Los Angeles

Publisher's ISBN: 0-87477-075-0 (paper)
                       0-87477-076-9 (case)

Design: Mike Yazzolino
Assistant: John Brogna
Additional Photographs: Bill Dobbins (pages 11, 27, 83, 89, 168)
Photographs on page 3: left, Vatican; right, Alinari–Scala
Manufactured in the United States of America

Published by J. P. Tarcher, Inc.
9110 Sunset Blvd., Los Angeles, Calif. 90069
Published simultaneously in Canada by Macmillan of Canada
70 Bond St., Toronto, Canada M5B 1X3

Q 10 9 8 7 6

The authors would like to thank Pete Samra, Kent Kuehn, and Jim Larson for their expertise and contributions to the text, and Merri Skrdla for her patience.

To Joe Weider and all the other champions
who train at Gold's

Contents

It was true for the Greeks and for Michaelangelo's models and it's true for us: Muscles were designed to be exercised and, when they are, they both look and feel better. The fastest and most efficient way of getting muscles into the proper condition is with weight training.

Weight training and its effects on the human body is a subject that has always been surrounded by myth, misinformation, and general confusion. Modern scientific and medical investigation of weight training vindicates it as a method of achieving overall physical fitness as well as strength.

No two bodies are alike and no two weight-training programs should be either. Knowing how to tailor the program to your own needs is as important as knowing how to perform the individual exercises.

You can't run a racing car on low-octane fuel, and you can't create a strong, good-looking body without understanding what food is and how it affects you.

The key to avoiding injury in weight training is to follow a graduated, progressive system of exercise that allows the body to get into condition and grow strong before any great stress is put upon it.

You and Weights

JOIN THE GOLD'S GYM CROWD

Gold's Gym is the premier bodybuilding gym in the world. In the last Mr. America contest, 5 out of the top 6 competitors worked out at Gold's including the winner, Dave Johns. Such international stars as Arnold Schwarzenegger, Lou Ferrigno, Robby Robinson, Franco Columbu, Serge Nubret, Ed Corney — in fact, every major national and international title holder — have trained at Gold's.

More bodies are shaped, muscles built, waists trimmed, thighs sculpted, and iron pumped at Gold's than any other place — possibly in the history of mankind. The reason for this is simple. Gold's builds bodies knowledgeably and scientifically, and that knowledge is available to you in this book.

Although Gold's is synonymous with strong, healthy, and beautiful bodies, if you go there expecting to see a room full of super bodybuilders only, you are in for a surprise. The professionals are much in evidence, of course, but these days you could just as well run into a next door neighbor, the family doctor, or the supermarket produce man. Add to the list numerous dancers, actors and actresses, athletes of all kinds, factory workers, housewives, and even the physically handicapped, and you have a better idea of what's really happening there.

Gold's has become a mecca for people from all walks of life who share with the professionals a single key idea: the body responds to a planned program of weight training. It changes shape, gets stronger and healthier. And its proud owner finds him or herself looking terrific, physically strong and confident and feeling great.

The motives that bring people to weight training are as varied as their lifestyles and professions. But they all know, many from personal experience, that neglected muscles become flaccid and shapeless and a neglected body becomes weak and often sick. And while most play tennis, jog, swim, or engage in other physical activities on a regular basis, they are aware that only certain muscles receive the benefit of these unsystematic exertions. The body's full potential for form and fitness can be realized only by an organized program affecting the entire body — the Gold's Gym system of progressive weight training.

A few short sessions with weights per week, according to the plan outlined in these pages, can put you in control of how your body looks, feels, and performs. The goal is maximum gain in minimum time, through planning, nutrition, and the principle of progressive resistance. These methods and the return of pride in physical form have combined to create the Gold's Gym phenomenon.

Pride in the Body Beautiful

The message from Gold's is as ancient as the classic nudity of Greek sculpture or the ideal form of Michelangelo's *David*: the body is good. Its development is not only physically and emotionally rewarding, but aesthetically pleasing as well.

We don't know if Greek athletes and models used weights to develop their bodies. But we do know that every major town had its Gold's Gym — the palaestra or gymnasium where wrestlers and others dedicated themselves to physical culture. The Olympic games (then played in the nude) and countless statues of outstandingly proportioned men and women testify to the ancient world's respect for the human form.

What about the notion that pride is a sin and vanity a weakness of character? Just think about it. What can possibly be wrong with looking and feeling your best? Take your cue from the Greeks, Michelangelo, and all those good people at Gold's. After a few centuries of doubt, we are again being invited to take pride in our bodies, and not just because they're fit and healthy, but because they look good, too.

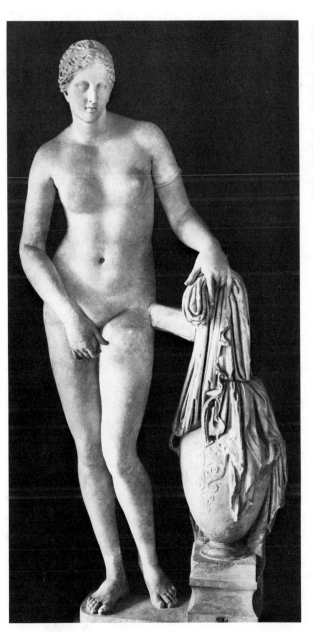

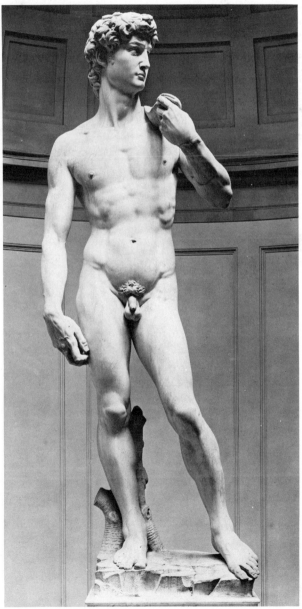

WEIGHT TRAINING IS NOT WEIGHTLIFTING

Don't confuse weight training with weightlifting or competitive bodybuilding — though it is the way serious body builders start. Few of the people at Gold's intend to bench press 600 pounds, grow a 20-inch bicep, or become Miss, Mr., or Mrs. Universe. Those who enter competitions of this type do use weights, but their goals are different. Weight lifters concentrate on the specific muscles they will need in competition more than on balanced overall development. Body builders want to build muscles for competition, as big and fully developed as possible. They go far beyond the proportions that most people who train their bodies with weights would consider desirable.

Weight training means the coordinated use of weights to shape, strengthen, and condition the body in an integrated way. The Gold's program will not prepare you for an Olympic weightlifting competition. It won't prepare you to be a Mr. America either — you need years of dedication for that — but you will look and feel better and be able to perform well in any activity requiring muscular strength if you follow it through. And you'll have achieved these results in the quickest, most efficient way.

Anyone Can Do It

Don't worry about what you are like now. Neither age nor present physical condition should discourage you. If you're in your middle years and out of condition, of course you'll have to start slowly and build gradually. But before you know it you'll be looking younger and feeling stronger. If you're under 14, you should use light weights to learn and practice the basic techniques. When your bones and muscles are mature, then you'll be fully ready to benefit from the progressive program. But whatever your age or style of life, weight training has something for you.

If you're a teenager, weight training will help you have a more attractive, stronger, and healthier body and improve your performance in sports. The body you build now will have a lot to do with the body you live in for the rest of your life.

If you're a young man, weight training can help you keep your youthful shape and condition when school and work cut into your time for active exercise.

If you're a young woman, weight training will provide a new sense of confidence and competence in all your activities. It's a convenient way to trim down or build up various parts of your body.

If you're in your thirties, suffering the effects of an inactive lifestyle, weight training can slim you down, firm you up, and make you feel a lot better.

If you have to do household chores, weight training will lighten the workload by giving you extra strength and energy.

If you're in your middle years, weight training can help retard the aging process and keep you looking and feeling youthful.

If you're an older person, weight training can help you keep your body supple, active, and physically sure.

If you're an athlete, no matter what your sport, weight training can improve your performance.

If you're an exercise dropout, discouraged by a lack of visible improvement from other programs, noticeable results of progressive resistance weight training will soon have you back in the fold.

If you're physically handicapped — in a wheelchair, for example — weight training can help you compensate by strengthening the rest of your body and improving your mobility and general health.

Watch and Listen to Your Body

The rewards of weight training arrive quickly. Your own body tells you what you're getting from the program and encourages you to keep working toward your personal goals.

You start to feel different
This happens soon, sometimes after the first workout. Your body feels more alive. You're less tired, more invigorated. Your muscles feel firmer and more responsive. You feel as if you're in better condition — and you are!

You get stronger

Within weeks you find that you can pick up and easily carry things that felt heavy before. Changing the distilled-water bottle no longer fills you with anxiety. The groceries or the luggage seem to have lost weight. And you no longer feel worn out by physical exertion.

Your appearance changes

Your proportions improve. Flab begins to disappear. You lose inches in some places — and if you want, gain them in others. Your muscles firm. Your friends (and even strangers) begin to mention how good you look.

The weight trainer's bonus

When you work your muscles strenuously with weights, you can actually feel the extra blood rushing into them and swelling them up. This feeling is called a "pump" and it's one of the extra rewards of weight training. It's a strong feeling of well-being in the right use of the body. It's the "high" of weight training.

Trade In Your Obsolete Body-Image

Confidence in your body and a positive body-image are important elements in the make-up of your personality. It's hard to feel happy about yourself if you don't like your body.

Weight training helps give you the feeling that you *are* your body, not just *in* it. Instead of a mind trapped in a reluctant prison of flesh, you are a mind/body totality. Your body is no longer something you drag along or something that holds you back. Instead it becomes the vehicle that carries you forward, responding strongly and competently when you call on it. It no longer resists activity but revels in it.

How you look doesn't just affect the way you feel, it also affects how other people treat you. Like it or not, people judge in large part on the basis of appearances. How you look is a basic part of your social identity and as you change and improve the look of your body you will see a change in the attitude of people you come into contact with.

These days there aren't many things in life that an individual can control. You may not be able to lower your taxes or avoid the next rise in the price of gas, but you can become the master of your own body. You can change how you look and feel.

You can trade in your present body for a new, improved model through the Gold's Gym weight-training program.

HOW WEIGHT TRAINING WORKS

Legend has it that Milo of Crotona decided to become the strongest man in the world. He hit upon the idea of starting with a calf and lifting it *every* day until it became a mature bull. As the calf got heavier, resistance to Milo's efforts increased, and he became stronger and stronger.

We use the same principle at Gold's today, only we use barbells instead of bulls, and we call it "progressive resistance exercise"; you train with progressively heavier weights as you become stronger. You'll see that, for each exercise, we recommend using an amount of weight that just barely lets you get through the program in 15 minutes. When you get stronger and it becomes easier to get through the workout, you simply increase the weight until the routine is difficult again.

Weight training works fast and efficiently because it employs the "overload" principle: giving a muscle more weight than it's accustomed to but *not* more than it can handle, thereby making it work as hard as possible for short periods of time. Progressive resistance weight training is therefore extremely efficient, getting this necessary work out of the muscles so that you get *maximum results in minimum time.*

The Unique Role of Weight Training

One way to fully appreciate the benefit of weight training is to compare it to other ways to keep fit that have caught the public fancy. Each has its benefits and its liabilities.

Cardiovascular programs are designed to increase the efficiency of your heart, lungs and circulation. Almost anything that makes you breathe harder and your pulse race is a beneficial cardiovascular exercise.

Running, swimming, bicycling, and rowing are particularly good for the cardiovascular system. So is weight training done in the Gold's Gym manner. But running or riding a bicycle does little for the muscles of the arms, shoulders, back and chest. Activities like rowing stress certain muscles but not others. Swimming is great exercise, but your muscles don't work against progressive resistance — the water never gets thicker and harder to swim through. These forms of exercise are good for you but can't work, develop, and shape the entire body as a system like the Gold's Gym program of weight training does.

Stretching programs operate on the theory that the greatest benefit to the body is achieved by stretching the muscles to make them more limber.

There isn't any doubt that being limber is good for you. Yoga and some other types of stretching programs help condition your muscles and prevent injuries. Stretching is particularly good for you if you're involved with weight training and doing a lot of exercises involving muscular contraction. But simply stretching the muscles of the body doesn't change their shape or proportions, doesn't make them stronger, and unless done with great vigor, involves no cardiovascular benefit.

Calisthenics force the body to work against its own weight in movements like push-ups, deep-knee bends, and jumping jacks.

This is essentially a kind of weight training done with a fixed weight — the amount you happen to weigh at the time. Calisthenics work your muscles and give you some cardiovascular benefit, but because they lack the principle of progressive resistance, they are a lot less efficient than weight-training techniques. They take as much time as weight training but result in fewer benefits, so they're a poor investment of your time unless you're someplace where equipment isn't available.

Isometrics put maximum stress on the muscles by pitting them against immovable objects, such as a wall, post, or even other muscles.

It used to be thought that this method increased strength a lot faster than traditional isotonic methods, in which the muscles are worked with uniform tension through an entire movement. But recent research doesn't bear this out. Isometrics do make you stronger but it's hard to tell how much, since you don't get the feedback you do with weights, which tell you immediately when you can handle more.

There are two other disadvantages of isometrics. Your muscles are firmed but not shaped: the distance you move a muscle as you're exercising it is vital to give it shape and in isometric exercises there is no movement at all. Also, there is no cardiovascular benefit: the exercises last for only about six seconds and cardiovascular conditioning requires at least ten minutes of continuous exertion.

Machines and gimmicks aren't made to do the full body job. We live in an age of machines and a lot of people like to use them for exercise. Some of them are pretty good but most aren't worth the cost. The best exercise machines are the home gyms put out by companies like Universal and Nautilus, but they cost a couple of thousand dollars. As for all those other devices that feature springs and pulleys, gauges and lots of chrome — they can't do a thing for you that can't be done better with a set of weights and the Gold's Gym program. If you have a device that you pull or compress, it will exercise certain muscles. But a good weight-training program trains *all* of the muscles, not just a few; it puts them through several different movements to bring out their full shape; it gives you strength as well as cardiovascular benefits.

Sports and recreational activities such as tennis, jogging, football or swimming provide definite physical-fitness benefits. Besides, they're fun so you don't have to grit your teeth and do them " just because they're good for you."

If you get a chance to play a lot of different sports, so much the better; few do. Most of us have days or weeks when we just don't have the opportunity. That results in a loss of condition. Also, playing a sport means that you use certain muscles in certain ways and a lot of parts of the body are hardly ever involved.

Weight training is very good combined with sports because it makes you stronger and better able to hit the ball or make the tackle and you can use it to maintain your conditioning on a daily basis. Weight training also stresses and develops the muscles that would otherwise not get much use. Most professional althletes use weight training to get better at what they do. (See Chapter Ten: Weight and Sports.) It will work for you, too.

Weight training is the answer to every body's needs.

Weight Training—Myths and Facts

THE LURKING DOUBT

If weight training is that great, why isn't everyone doing it? The fact is that more and more people *are* taking up weight training, as a peek into Gold's and other gyms and health clubs around the country will show. But some, and women especially, continue to be discouraged by a persistent collection of misunderstandings and false conceptions about it. Most of these potential weight trainers are not aware that the experiences of countless individuals, as well as scientific and medical studies, have already laid these myths to rest.

Nowadays the benefits and liabilities of any physical fitness program can be methodically measured and proved. Whenever weight trainers have been pitted against athletes using other training systems, they have scored well in the ability to do work, in cardiovascular and muscular endurance, and in the small percentage of fat in their body composition. This is true for both men and women.

Why then do the old myths hang on? Obviously not everyone has heard the scientific evidence vindicating weight training as a path to physical fitness. It takes time for fact to replace a well-worn rumor. But simple ignorance is not always the explanation. Let's face it, weight training — like any exercise — involves work. It's always easier to let yourself be discouraged by someone's negative opinion than to start picking up weights.

Everyone has been exposed to some of the following myths about weight training but very few have ever heard them refuted. Because women particularly have been misinformed, we've included a special section on the traditional worries that used to keep them from the benefits of weight training.

Now let's look at the myths that we hear all the time — and the facts that refute them.

MYTH: Weight Training Will Make Me Muscle Bound

"Muscle bound" is not a medical term — it has no scientific meaning. It reflects the belief that working the muscles can make them tight, thereby creating a body that is clumsy, awkward, and unathletic. If this were true most N.F.L. football players would be clumsy, awkward, and unathletic because every team has a much used weightroom.

When you contract one muscle in weight training you automatically stretch another. If you're using an effective all-body program of weight training, the result is as much stretching and loosening as tightening and contracting, making for added grace and ease of motion. The truth is that professional and collegiate athletes in every sport, including those that require the greatest agility, like basketball, gymnastics, track and field, and tennis, work out with weights as part of the regular training program.

MYTH: Weight Training Will Make Me Heavier

There are two ways to understand "heavier"—adding pounds or getting fat. The two don't always go together. If you lounge in an armchair all day wolfing bonbons, you'll get fat. If you train with weights according to the Gold's system, you'll be burning off fat and gaining muscle. Most people lose a few pounds or maintain about the same number when they weight train. Some will weigh more, but in all the right places. Weight training lets you put the weight where you want it and eliminate it where you don't. Everyone will replace unsightly bulges with attractive, useful muscle fiber — which might weigh more than fat, but looks and feels a lot better.

The issue is not just the number on a scale, but the shape, definition, and proportion you want your body to have. If you've got firm arms, a slim waist, and lean athletic thighs, you can throw the scale out the window.

MYTH: Weight Trainers' Muscles Are Really Useless

This myth, possibly stemming from envy, is that exercises that give you good definition and muscular shape somehow don't really make you strong. The idea probably originated from the fact that competitive bodybuilders are generally not quite as strong as competitive weightlifters of the same weight. This happens because the weightlifter trains with heavier weights and tries to become as strong as possible, while keeping his own weight within the limits of his competitive class. A bodybuilder, because he is more interested in an aesthetic goal rather than a purely athletic one, may even deliberately gain weight and doesn't necessarily attempt to work with very heavy weights while shaping his body.

Anyone who has done any weight training knows it makes you stronger. One of the ways you'll keep track of your progress is by how much weight you're able to handle in various exercises. The stronger you get, the more weight you'll train with. When you're able to add five or ten pounds to an exercise, your own body will disprove this myth.

MYTH: Weight Training Will Make Me Too Big

When new people come in to sign up for a program at Gold's they often go out of their way to say, "Oh, I want to get in

shape, but I don't want to get *too* big." Sometimes we have to hide a smile because we know just what's on their minds. They are thinking, of course, of the kind of physique attained by the competitive bodybuilders who also train at the Gym.

To most people, a bodybuilder's physique is so strange and unusual that they think it grotesque. But regardless of taste, being afraid of getting too big when you start out weight training is like beginning piano lessons and expressing a fear of becoming a virtuoso. In both cases, the answer is—fat chance.

Weight training, when done properly and combined with the right kind of diet, will cause muscular growth. Men can achieve quite a bit of size increase, women only a slight amount, because it is the male hormone that causes the growth. But the kind of physique associated with a Mr. America is only achieved by years of single-minded, dedicated effort. A competitive bodybuilder trains up to four hours a day and has to be extremely careful of diet, alternately stuffing or starving his body depending on how close the next contest is. Bodybuilding on that level is the most brutal, grueling and demanding discipline around, except perhaps for marathon running. Fifteen minutes of training a day does not a Mr. America make. The goals of our weight-training program are shape, strength and fitness, not a 54-inch chest. Some may want to go on and eventually add a lot of muscular bulk, but that's another kind of training.

MYTH: If I Stop Training My Muscles Will Turn to Fat

Another widely held misconception is reinforced when people see former athletes who are now fat, flabby, and gone to seed. It seems to many that they are seeing a lot of unused muscle that has turned into fat and they're afraid to develop their own bodies because they fear the same thing might happen to them.

From a physiological point of view, muscle is muscle and fat is fat — one can't possibly turn into the other. What usually happens is that an athlete who has been active all his life suddenly finds himself retired and fails to modify his diet to fit his new lifestyle. He just keeps eating. The more active you are the more calories you can consume without gaining weight. When you stop being active, you have to eat less or you'll get fat. Muscle tends to lose bulk when you stop training, but it doesn't turn into anything else.

MYTH: I'll Hurt Myself

People who don't know anything about weight training are understandably fearful of picking up heavy weights and hurting themselves. They hear words like "hernia" or "sprain" and it turns them away. Certainly, if you grab a barbell and don't know what you're doing, you're definitely risking injury. But that isn't what we recommend. We want you to follow the program step by step, to learn to do each exercise carefully and with the proper amount of weight.

When beginning a program of weight training, you don't pick up heavy weights. (Many people start using just a bar without any weights on it.) Only as you become stronger do you gradually increase the amount of weight you use in each exercise. Far from making you susceptible to injuries, your increasing strength, endurance, and flexibility will actually help prevent them — not only while you're training with weights, but in sports and daily activities as well. It's no secret that special weight-training programs are also used to repair and rehabilitate muscles and joints injured in football or other sports.

MYTH: If I Lift Weights People Will Consider Me Self-Centered

The many mirrors one sees at Gold's and other weight training gyms serve extremely practical purposes. They help the weight trainer improve on concentration, form, and balance, and allow the bodybuilders to study shape and proportion — which is, after all, what that activity is all about.

There is, of course, a strong element of ego satisfaction in competitive body building, but no more so than in any effort to become something that one wants to be. There is also pride, dedication, a willingness to sacrifice, and lots of other virtues that go with any achievement. Weight training, however, is a number of steps short of competitive body building, and there's no more ego-centeredness in it than there is in the activity of the dieter or jogger who's working on his or her body.

Weight training isn't for the self-centered though some self-centered people do it as they do every other activity. It is for the self-concerned, for those who've decided that it's time to improve the way they look and feel. It's a program for people who really care about themselves, who want to look better and be more attractive to other people, and to be healthier and live longer.

THE WONDER WOMAN SYNDROME

For a long time in our society, women have suffered from the pressure to be physically appealing, but at the same time not too active; capable of hard work, yet not too strong. This contradictory image is rapidly losing ground, but there are still modern women who draw the line at weight training as an activity and exercise. Fear of muscle bulk and perhaps distaste for the "macho" image associated with weights have put them off.

An increasing number of the strenuous exercise programs for women, however, do include weights. The Golden Door in Escondido, California, is a good example of an internationally famous health spa that has incorporated progressive resistance exercise into its women's fitness plan. There, members alternate weight training exercises with other types for breath and circulation benefits as well as using "circuit training" or continuous movement exercises like that of the Gold's system. Now literally thousands of women's health clubs around the country offer weight exercises as part of their fitness program. Still, the negative myths linger on, keeping women from using weights. Let's tackle them one by one.

MYTH: Weights Can't Improve a Woman's Strength, Because Women Are Naturally Weak

The average male is 30 to 40 percent stronger than the average female. This generalization is only true for overall body strength. Looking at specific parts of the body, leg strength is almost the same in women as in men and, taking relative weight into consideration, women are often relatively stronger. In upper-body strength men can easily be twice as strong as women.

It is said that women don't use their muscles as much as men do, and so they don't get as strong. What happens to them if they undertake a program of weight training? According to Professor Jack H. Wilmore of the University of Arizona: "A recent study has demonstrated that the mean strength of young, nonathletic women can be improved by as much as 30 percent by a ten-week weight training program. Some of the women in this study doubled their strength in selected areas during this relatively short training period. In comparison with a group of nonathletic young men on an identical program, these women exhibited greater gains in strength, although their initial strength values were lower."

Wilmore has conducted studies indicating that women are capable of matching men in endurance and cardiovascular fitness, can achieve equal levels of strength in many body parts, and can come within 10 percent of men's strength in others. In other words, the notion that women are so much weaker than men is not a physiological fact but probably the result of the next fallacy.

MYTH: Strength Is Not Feminine

It starts early. Women are told that strength is somehow not "ladylike," that exercise, for them, is more a social outlet than a basic, physical necessity. They get caught in a vicious circle as they're told they're weak and then encouraged to live in such a way as to become weaker. Ironically, this attitude eventually leads to the loss of the shape, allure and health of an attractive, feminine figure.

Bodies don't age as quickly when they are exercised — properly. But many exercise programs, supposedly aimed at helping women keep the allure of a youthful body, actually make things worse by substituting nonstrenuous activity for a good, hard workout, thereby lulling many women into thinking they're making progress when they aren't. The fact remains that all bodies need to be stressed to be healthy and strong — and that's as true for women as it is for men.

MYTH: Weight Training Builds Bulk in Women

However much the average woman or even the female athlete would like to firm, strengthen and shape her body, one thing she definitely doesn't want is to add any great degree of muscular bulk. Except in extremely rare cases, she has nothing to worry about. A man's muscles increase in mass because his body contains high levels of testosterone, the male sex hormone. With very little of this hormone in her body, the average woman can expect little if any gain in muscle size. Weight training, in fact, tends to slim women. Coupled with the proper diet, it helps eliminate fat. Since a woman generally has a relatively greater amount of fat than does a man, the loss of it can result in some truly dramatic slimming. But weight training is important because merely losing fat isn't enough — it's necessary to tone the muscles and give them an attractive shape for maximum benefit.

Be in Command of Your Body

Most women don't want to be the feminine equivalent of the Six Million Dollar Man, but *feeling* like $6 million is a goal everyone can appreciate. The Gold's Gym program is designed to trim, slim, and shape feminine figures, but there's a bonus: you'll notice an automatic improvement in how you feel and in your athletic ability, an increase in performance on the tennis court and the golf course. When you're fit and strong, games and athletic activity become a lot more fun.

And there will be practical advantages in other areas as well. There's an independence to be enjoyed in being able to move a piece of furniture, lift a box, open a jar and carry groceries without help.

Women have as much to gain from weight training as men. A strong body is healthy, youthful, attractive, and graceful. It just works that way, a gift from that ultimate feminist, Mother Nature.

Jan Todd, considered the world's strongest woman, sums up her reasons for weight training: "I think strength and femininity are inseparable. I lift because I love it. I love the way it makes me feel. It has extended my idea of what is possible for me." And for countless weight training women it has done the same — as it can for you.

Your Program

WHAT DO YOU WANT TO LOOK LIKE?

No two bodies are exactly alike, and no two people have precisely the same goals as to how they want to look. The Gold's Gym program explains how your body can be shaped and trained, and then shows how you can use the program to achieve your own personal goals.

The beginning of the program is the same for everyone, but as you progress, you'll be given more and more opportunity to make your own choices about which exercises to do to shape and strengthen specific parts of your body. Using the Gold's Gym program can develop your body to its fullest — you can make yourself into the best possible you.

At each level we will give you new movements to perform, and some new ways to do exercises you've already learned. Doing a movement one way instead of another, using a barbell instead of dumbbells, turning your body this way instead of that can sometimes make a substantial and marvelous difference.

When you follow the program, you will progress gradually from basic levels to more advanced ones strictly at your own pace. When you feel you have mastered the program at a given level, *you* will decide when it's time to move on. By the time you have reached the most advanced level, you will fully understand how to exercise, train, and shape all the parts of your body.

WHAT YOU GET

Within the range chosen by each individual, the Gold's Gym program provides everyone with three basic benefits:

Cardiovascular conditioning to benefit your respiratory and circulatory systems;

Muscular conditioning through the use of progressive resistance exercises; and

Diet and nutrition information to prepare your body to profit fully from the exercises.

Cardiovascular Benefit

Your heart is a muscle and needs to be exercised like any other. The traditional ways of training with weights don't provide cardiovascular conditioning. When you lift a heavy weight a few times, then stop to rest, you do get stronger but you don't build up a lot of endurance. This kind of training is fine for a competition weightlifter, but a person who is taking up weight training to look better, feel better, and become more fit requires exercise that accelerates the heart rate for periods of 10 minutes or more, thereby building up cardiovascular strength.

The stronger your heart is the longer it will last. That's why cardiovascular conditioning is so important — and why the Gold's Gym program uses a Peripheral Heart Action (P.H.A.) circuit training system. Circuit training means you go from one exercise to another essentially without stopping. Each of the exercises is done with moderate weight and many repetitions. You train continuously for no more than 15 minutes, exercise virtually all the muscles of the body, and experience tremendous cardiovascular benefits.

When your heart is made to beat faster over a period of time, it gets stronger. The normal heart rate varies from person to person, but is approximately 70 to 80 beats a minute. A rate of 120 to 140 or even more can be achieved by heavy exercise.

You can check your pulse rate by feeling for the artery at your wrist or in your neck, just beside the Adam's apple. Instead of counting for a full minute, it's quicker to count for 6 seconds and multiply by 10. If you want to keep track of your cardiovascular fitness over a period of time, check:

- *What your normal heart rate is when not exercising*
- *How high a rate you achieve by strenuous exercise*
- *How long it takes after you finish exercising for your heart rate to return to normal*

By keeping a record of the above information you will quickly discover the benefits of cardiovascular exercise — a somewhat slower normal basic heartbeat than you now have, and a quicker return to that normal rate when you are finished exercising.

Muscular Conditioning

When you put stress on your muscles with progressive resistance exercise, you enjoy two basic benefits:

Increased strength, which comes as a result of incrementally overloading the muscle, and

Improved shape, which happens when you work a muscle through its full range of movement, constantly changing the angle of stress and distributing tension along the length of the muscle.

When you train with weights there are two variables involved with each exercise: how much weight you use, and how many repetitions you do. Generally, the more weight you use, the stronger you'll get; the more repeitions you do, the more your muscle is conditioned. As we have already promised, once you've started the Gold's Gym program you'll notice some changes in yourself: you can walk up a flight of stairs without getting out of breath, carry groceries with increased ease, and play sports without waking up the next morning feeling sore and stiff. In addition to these signs, you can follow your progress by keeping records on a training chart.

| GOLD'S TRAINING ROUTINE | | | | | | | | | LEVEL 1 | |
| SHOULDER PRESS DEAD LIFTS UPRIGHT ROWS | | | BENT OVER ROWS SQUATS CURLS | | | | | | LEG RAISES | |
DATE	CIRC.	WT.	DATE	CIRC.	WT.	DATE	CIRC.	WT.	DATE	NO.

Weight lifted

As you get stronger you'll find you can perform the exercises using more weight. New members of Gold's Gym are given charts on which to keep track of the exercises they do and how much weight they use for each one. This kind of chart is useful in giving you a quick, visual reference as to how far and how quickly you have progressed.

The scale

Whether you're over, under or exactly your ideal weight, the Gold's Gym program can help you. Weighing yourself regularly gives you a continuous idea of what effect the program is having on your body. Day to day variations of a pound or two may not be significant, since your body's retention of fluids can easily make that much difference. Real weight gain or loss is a slow process and should be measured over a period of weeks or months.

The tape measure

Your overall weight is not an accurate gauge of the changes brought about by weight training. Often you can gain some muscle weight and lose some fat and the scale won't register any change. It's a much better idea to use a tape measure in conjunction with the scale to guage all the subtle differences weight training is making to your body.

Before you start the program, measure the size of your waist, chest, upper arms, hips, thighs, calves, or any other area of the body about which you are concerned. Record these measurements and your current weight in a notebook. After about six weeks (or whenever you think significant changes may have taken place) measure yourself again and compare the two sets of figures. Don't expect changes to take place too quickly or expect to make gains at a uniform rate. Sometimes your body will respond quickly and other times it won't.

The mirror

Since the Gold's Gym program is designed in part to change your appearance, you have to look at yourself to see the difference. That's where the mirror comes in: you use it to see how the parts of your body are responding and which could use a little more work. When you look in the mirror you'll see that you are looking more like the person you have been training to become. That is the strongest motivation for staying with the program that we know.

All of these things we've mentioned — the amount of weight you can lift, the scale, tape measure, and the mirror — are extremely valuable in letting you know what kind of results you're getting from the Gold's Gym program. But there's another, entirely different kind of feedback you should be prepared for: that look in people's eyes when they notice the changes in your body, the look of surprise or even envy on some faces, the look of pleasure and delight in the eyes of someone you're close to. There's no chart needed to keep track of this weight training benefit.

With all of these benefits available through weight training, your tendency may be (as it is with ninety percent of the people who take up this form of exercise) to try to do too much too soon. That's why we've designed the Gold's Gym program to be "progressive," allowing you to get used to a certain level of effort before giving you more to do. The tortoise never develops cardiovascular fitness, but as we learned in the fable, the hare can easily burn himself out. When you start getting results from weight training, the response can be to throw yourself into it with increased zeal. Don't. Pace your training. A moderate program when done consistently over a period of time will provide better results than a fast and furious one done only intermittently. Increase your training gradually. Add exercises slowly and you'll go further, last longer, and be a lot happier with the results.

Diet and Nutrition

Food is both fuel and building material to the body. How and what you eat can drastically affect your health and your body's ability to benefit from exercise.

Modern nutritionists frequently disagree about the need for different kinds of food, vitamin and mineral supplements, protein, and various kinds of weight gain or weight loss diets, but there are basics that anyone can learn — and learn to apply. The Gold's Gym program will provide that information: what food is, what it does to you, and how you can get your body to look the way you want by changing your dietary habits. (See Chapter Four: Food for Strength and Beauty.)

Food for Strength and Beauty

EATING THE GOLD'S GYM WAY

Every year athletes get bigger, stronger, and faster. Records continue to be broken. Coaches, trainers, and athletes credit the gains as much to advances in nutritional knowledge as to improved equipment and training. When you decided to train with weights, you made the decision to appreciate and care for your body. Whether you want to build up firm muscles or lose fat and shape your body, paying attention to proper nutrition is an important part of the Gold's Gym system.

The program not only attacks the excess fat but also improves the shape of the new thinner you. It's a cooperative effort involving knowledge of nutritional values, modified eating habits, and weight training exercise.

Like the exercises themselves, Gold's nutritional recommendations respect the unity of the body. Starvation or fad diets, by the simple logic of energy input and output, can reduce excess fat. But they offer no guarantee of improved shape, health, or fitness. And sometimes they do positive harm by treating the body not as a system but merely as a conglomeration of fat deposits to be starved or burned away.

People who train at Gold's are given nutritional guidance as well as exercise instruction. "The first thing I do is ask newcomers what their eating habits are," says Pete Samra, one of the managers of the gym and a nutritional expert. "Then I suggest a well-balanced diet with sufficient high-quality protein, carbohydrates from fruits and vegetables, polyunsaturated fats, and some vitamin and mineral supplements. They should also be sure to drink enough liquids, and I always tell them to stay away from white bread — refined flour in general — and processed sugar."

Sometimes instructions like these raise more questions than they answer: What does well-balanced mean? How much protein must I have? What exactly are carbohydrates? What kinds of vitamins and minerals do I need?

Basic Food Facts

Though we eat several times every day, most of us don't know much about food and what it does to us and for us. Some knowledge of the subject is vital if you want to get maximum benefits from your weight-training program, and learn to control the form and feel of your body. Food has several physical functions. It provides energy for the activities of the body and mind. It makes possible the growth, maintenance, and repair of tissues. Certain foods aid in the regulation of specific internal body processes.

Good basic nutrition (a balanced diet) requires a variety of foods from four basic food groups: (1) milk and milk products; (2) meats and other sources of protein such as fish, eggs, cheese, dry beans or nuts; (3) vegetables and fruits; (4) breads and cereals. Your body uses seven different kinds of nutrients, if you include water and air. The others are protein, carbohydrates, fats, vitamins, and minerals. Some would also include fiber.

Protein

Protein's main function in the body is the building, maintenance, and replacement of tissue, especially muscle. Thus our protein needs are greater when we are growing, when we have suffered injury, and when we undertake a program such as weight training to reshape and strengthen our body.

The Department of Agriculture recommends about 70 grams of protein daily for an adult male of average size (150–160 pounds) and about 10 grams less for a woman in the average 130-pound range. Another norm based on one gram of protein for each kilogram of body weight would give our average man and woman 65 and 55 grams respectively, with a double requirement for times of tissue building and repair.

The Gold's recommendation for anyone in a weight-training program is one gram of protein for each pound of body weight. Thus a 150-pound person would be expected to consume about 150 grams of protein daily. The increased protein is for tissue development — and is often supplemented by other energy sources to meet the increased demands of weight-training exercise. What one doesn't get from his regular diet can be made up with protein powders, the least expensive and most dependable of which is nonfat dry milk solids. (A government guide mentioned later in this chapter will give you all the information you need on the protein, carbohydrate and fat values in various foods.)

Meat, eggs, and dairy products are called complete proteins because they contain all eight of the essential amino acids. Dried beans and nuts are also a good source. Vegetable sources such as wheat germ or nutritional yeast do not fulfill this norm. But they are still good protein and in certain combinations are indistinguishable from animal varieties.

The famous liquid-protein diets are not only dangerous, but completely irrelevant to our purposes. You need a balance of fats and carbohydrates for energy. If they are lacking, protein will be diverted from its muscle-building function to provide fuel for muscular work.

Carbohydrates

These are primary sources of energy and a vital element in brain chemistry. Carbohydrates (fruits, vegetables, whole grains and cereals) are converted in the mouth and small intestine to simple blood sugar or glucose. Refined or raw sugar and honey are also carbohydrates and of similar chemical composition. They are a source of quick but short-lived energy, and they provide no nutritional benefit. In excess amounts they convert quickly into fat. If you have a sweet tooth, you'd be better off with a piece of fruit or a glass of fruit juice than with a candy bar.

Blood sugar level is related to the feeling of hunger, so an intake of carbohydrates will quiet the pangs temporarily. But more important is an adequate continued supply of carbohydrates — no more than 100 grams daily for active weight trainers — combined with the other elements of a balanced diet.

Fats

Much has been written of saturated, unsaturated, and poly-unsaturated fats, especially in relation to cholesterol and heart disease. It's enough to know that polyunsaturated fats from liquid oils of vegetable origin (corn, safflower, wheat germ, peanuts, soybeans, cottonseed) are generally better for you than animal fats or solid shortenings (saturated fats). Frying foods in vegetable oil doesn't help, because cooked oils become saturated.

A diet high in polyunsaturated fats and the regular exercise of weight training will help to keep body fat and cholesterol at normal levels. Fats are also an energy source, help the body assimilate fat-soluble vitamins like A, D, E, and K, and provide insulation and protection for body organs and structures. Sources include dairy products, oils, and red meat.

Vitamins and Minerals

A balanced diet from the four food groups should provide you with all the required vitamins and minerals in natural form. They are found particularly in fats and carbohydrates. But since food processing and certain cooking methods destroy some vitamins, it's reasonable to take a vitamin and mineral supplement that includes all essential elements (including trace minerals like iron and zinc).

The B-complex vitamins are involved in the metabolism of proteins, fats, and carbohydrates. Their deficiency has an almost immediate effect on muscular performance. Deficiencies of other vitamins take longer to slow up activity levels.

Water

A good water balance requires 6-7 glasses of fluid daily, and the replacement of liquid lost through perspiration. It's all right to replace water during activity sessions.

Fiber

Fiber is the indigestible parts of food that pass through our digestive systems unchanged. People on average diets already eat a quarter ounce a day and even the fiber enthusiasts are satisfied with a full ounce. To get more fiber in your diet, buy whole grain products, use brown rice instead of white, and eat pumpkin or sunflower seeds and nuts (not too many, they are high in calories). You can also increase the amount of fiber that you eat by not peeling cucumbers, eggplants, and apples, or straining orange or other citrus juice.

GOOD AND BAD HABITS

Knowing what to eat is important in gaining or losing weight. But real changes in your weight must be the result of new eating and nutritional habits. You can't change your diet for a few weeks, then go back to eating the way you did before. So, along with knowing what to eat, you should also understand *when* and *how* to eat.

When to Eat

Always try to eat a good breakfast

By the time you wake up the body has exhausted its supply of many of the nutrients it needs to get you through the day. You need a balanced breakfast with protein, carbohydrates, and fats. Toast and coffee aren't enough.

A word here on habit. If you aren't used to eating breakfast you won't feel hungry, but that doesn't mean you don't need breakfast.

Don't eat again until you're hungry

A lot of us are tempted by coffee breaks and social occasions and are pressured by circumstances into too-early lunches. Unless you're on a weight-gain program, let a grumbling stomach tell you when you're truly hungry.

Don't eat too close to your bedtime

When you eat late your body just won't use up all that fuel and will tend to store it as fat. So try not to eat any later than four hours before bedtime. When you're trying to lose weight, eating even earlier is better. If your schedule won't let you eat early, try to keep the meal light.

How to Eat

Eat smaller portions

Digestion takes time. When you're eating there's a delay between the time you've actually had enough and when your blood sugar level tells you that you aren't hungry any more. So you have to know how much food is enough and stop with that. In general, it's always better to have several small meals than a few big ones but if you want to gain weight, keep to smaller portions and eat four or five meals a day.

You don't always have to eat "meals"

Sometimes we don't have the feeling we've really eaten unless we're stuffed and can feel a big lump lying in our stomachs. But an orange, a handful of almonds and a piece of cheese can satisfy hunger and nutritional requirements without constituting a bulky, calorie-filled meal. Two or three light snacks like that are better for you than stuffing yourself all at once.

Make your last meal a moderate one

As we've discussed, your body doesn't need much fuel later on in the day. But dinner is traditionally the big meal in our society and there is a lot of temptation to overindulge: cocktails before dinner, wine or beer with, large portions of meat and potatoes, bread with the meal, dessert afterwards. This is especially true when we eat in a restaurant. That kind of eating is never healthful, and, at night, will insure that your body will store most of the excess as fat.

Save "special" foods for special occasions

We all have certain high-calorie foods that we love and would find hard to give up. But you don't have to give up French fries because they're high in saturated fats or ice cream because it contains so much sugar — you just have to cut down and have them only once in a while. If you allow yourself just one "forbidden" food every other day, your body can tolerate it and you won't have to give up anything entirely.

Frequently include low-fat poultry or fish on your menu

One of the reasons beef tastes so good is that it has a high fat content. So do meats like pork and lamb. Poultry, on the other hand, has good quality protein and little fat. Fish has even less. Try some turkey, chicken, or tuna fish instead of that steak or hamburger from time to time. That way you still get all the protein you need but you don't take in the extra calories and the saturated fats. If you prefer meats, veal is lower than beef in fat content.

Take your time and enjoy your meals

When you eat quickly you don't chew your food well, and hinder the digestive process. Even worse, you don't get to taste what you're eating. Give yourself enough time for your meal so you can relax and enjoy it. It's better for you — and a lot more enjoyable.

Keeping a Food Diary

When new members at Gold's ask for nutritional help we usually advise them to write down everything they eat for a couple of days and bring it in for us to look at. Sometimes they surprise themselves by seeing a pattern in the food diary that they didn't know existed. For instance, when you know that it takes 3500 calories to form one pound of body fat and that a jigger of whiskey contains 100 calories, it's easy to figure out that one drink of whiskey a day for a year amounts to almost twelve pounds which will have to be worked off if they are not going to stay on your body.

Of course, you only put on weight when you don't use up all the calories you take in. But in order to fully control your weight, you should have some idea of exactly how many calories you're getting in your food. Keeping a food diary helps. You may not want to bother with it for more than a few days, but that should be enough. What you do is:

• Write down everything you eat in the course of the day. If you're at home, weigh portions on a kitchen scale or check them with a measuring cup. If you're eating out, estimate the amount.

• Use a food guide to add up the number of calories in your meals as well as the number of grams of protein and carbohydrates. You can buy such guides at health food stores and general book stores or you can write to: Superintendent of Documents, U.S. Government Printing Office, Washington, D.C. 20402.

Ask for "Nutritive Value of Foods," Home and Garden

Bulletin no. 72, put out by the Department of Agriculture. This guide not only lists calories, protein and carbohydrates, but water and fatty acid content of foods and gives some vitamin and mineral information.

YOUR PERSONAL NUTRITION PROGRAM

To look and feel as good as possible, weight trainers need all the energy that good nutrition supplies. In the Gold's Gym program, you gradually progress to heavier weights and more strenuous exercises as you become ready for them. Your personal nutritional program should therefore also be gradual, but it must also be certain and sure.

As you begin to alter your eating habits, first look for the things you can give up with the least hardship. Most of us derive a lot of security from food and the way we eat and suddenly pulling out all the props isn't going to do any good. But a little change easily won can be the motivation for bigger changes accomplished with greater effort.

Good nutrition and weight training reinforce one another. When you eat well you have more energy and get more enjoyment from weight training. When you start looking and feeling better from weight training, you can become less emotionally reliant on food. Good nutrition accelerates the positive changes in your body which the weight training gives you, and the combination of the two helps you to arrive at a body weight that is right for you.

Since no two bodies are the same, neither are their nutritional requirements. One person might be able to eat ice cream every day and not gain weight while you may not. When you keep a food diary and otherwise pay attention to how the way you eat affects your body, you will be able to develop your own personal program of nutrition which will further your progress in weight training and help you look and feel better faster.

Weights and the Doctor

AN OUNCE OF WEIGHT TRAINING

There are a lot of injuries associated with the playing of sports, especially when the players are not in condition. But have you ever heard of "weight trainer's elbow," "lifter's knee," or "bodybuilder's shoulder"? Probably not, because weight training, when properly practiced for general conditioning, is one of the safest games in town. If you follow the instructions and procedures of the Gold's program, you'll not only avoid injury during weight-training sessions, but you'll also protect yourself against the perennial bugaboos of the weekend athlete: aching back, torn or strained muscles, sore joints, and so on.

Weight training prevents injury by increasing muscular conditioning in the whole body, making it stronger, tougher, and more flexible. The natural "cooperation" of muscles, joints, tendons, and ligaments in the body's activity is guaranteed through the systematic strengthening of weight training. Such chronic complaints as tennis shoulder, pitcher's elbow, or surfer's knee can thus be effectively avoided, and the pleasures of even once-a-week athletics maintained without anxiety.

And there's more. Weight training is flexible and selective. If you have had the misfortune to sustain injury in some sports activity, you can take it easy on sensitive areas, control precisely the amount of effort involved, and still work the rest of your body strenuously to maintain general conditioning.

Coaches who want to get an injured player back on the field as soon as possible hit upon the use of progressive resistance exercise for rehabilitation. The great advantage of weight training therapy is selectivity — the exercise can be focused on the problem area in the progressive quantity needed for gradual repair.

In the late 1940s Marlon Brando starred in *The Men*, a movie about the therapy undergone by paraplegic veterans of World War II. These men were encouraged to exercise and condition themselves because, no matter what their physical limitations, their bodies still required exercise and they could never recover their health without it. This is also true of people with less severe physical problems. Injury tends to make us less physically active and that lack of activity can often compound the problem.

AVOIDING INJURY

Even in a relatively safe activity like weight training, occasional injuries can occur and must be dealt with. Any stressful activity—whether lifting weights or moving furniture—involves the risk of minor injury to the unwary or the negligent. Most frequently the injuries that do occur are traceable directly to a mistake made by the suffering weight trainer. Perhaps he or she failed to take common-sense precautions, didn't warm up properly, drifted away from correct technique, or tried to work with too much weight.

The amount and type of weight should be carefully regulated in weight training. Experienced lifters know this, and beginners are taught to progress step by step. If you remember this principle, and follow the basic rules below, your closest encounter with torn ligaments or serious back injuries will probably be vicarious: watching them happen to some hapless quarterback on network TV.

Warm up thoroughly

Light exercising and stretching get the body ready and blood flowing into the muscles to facilitate the transportation of oxygen and nutrients.

Progress step by step

In the Gold's Gym program you progress gradually from one level to another. That's important. If you get ahead of yourself and try to do too many exercises too soon, or lift too much weight before you're ready, you're asking for trouble. Don't let your ego get involved; don't work with more weight than you should. And remember that you'll be stronger some days than others — just because you could handle a certain weight yesterday doesn't necessarily mean that you can handle it today, too. Pay attention to what your body is telling you.

Learn to concentrate
A number of injuries occur simply because somebody wasn't paying full attention to doing the exercise. If you concentrate, you'll minimize the chance of error. Be aware at all times of where the weight is and where your body is in relation to it.

Thinking about a movement as you do it keeps you from suddenly subjecting a muscle to unexpected strain. Concentration also helps you control and balance the weight, which is beneficial not only in preventing injury, but also in avoiding large dents in the floor.

Use correct technique
Never get careless. If you don't handle weights properly, you can put stress on the wrong part of the body and cause injury. Handle even light weights with respect. If you have a mirror available, you can use it to check your technique and to help your concentration as well.

Nobody's Perfect

If something should go wrong during a session, it's important to know what to do about it. Let's look at some potential problems and their care.

"Pulling" or "spraining" occurs when strain causes a hemorrhage or rupture to the tendon or muscle. Blood seeps into the area causing swelling and pain. This isn't usually serious but the discomfort can keep you from working out for several days or weeks — thereby setting you back in your program.

"Tendonitis" is an injury to the tendon itself and also results in pain and discomfort from hemorrhage and swelling.

"Bursitis" is an inflammation of the bursa, a sac found in a joint space. It also can occur because of strain. The resulting inflammation causes soreness and pain whenever the joint is moved or rotated.

These types of injuries are called "acute" because they happen suddenly rather than as a result of cumulative problems. The treatment for all of them is the same and fairly simple:

Apply cold to the inflamed area
An ice bag on the area during the first 24 to 48 hours after the injury restricts the capillaries and blood vessels and limits the hemorrhaging and, therefore, the pain. This is also a good treatment for a sprained ankle and wrist, torn Achilles tendon, pulled hamstring or torn muscles anywhere in your body.

Reduce the inflammation with medication
Aspirin will usually do the trick. If you need something more, you should consult your physician.

Rest the injured area

This is absolutely necessary. If you continue to put strain on the injured area you're not going to give it time to heal.

Apply heat to the injured area

This tends to relieve pain and speed recovery after the first 24 to 48 hour period. Keep in mind that even after the muscle, joint, or tendon begins to feel better it is still vulnerable. Get back into your program gradually and don't put too much sudden strain on that area or you risk a recurrence of the problem.

More Serious Injuries

Serious injuries usually don't occur if you don't make mistakes, but it's best to know about them just in case. Occasionally we run across torn muscles and ligaments, severe sprains, back problems, hernias, and dislocations. Each of these injuries is serious enough to warrant the attention of a doctor, but with proper treatment there is usually no long-term problem.

Many people fear hernias, but surprisingly few know what the term means. A hernia is a split or rip in the fibrous sheath of a muscle, much like the tear that might occur in a tight pair of pants when you suddenly bend over. The kind of hernia people associate with weights is an injury to the muscles of the abdominal wall. When the muscle splits, the inner contents emerge. Part of the intestines can creep out through the opening and become constricted. A hernia of this type is serious and should be treated by a doctor. Proper exercise tends to make you less vulnerable to this and other kinds of injury.

It makes good sense to be concerned about preventing injury, but don't let your worries interfere with getting all the benefits you can from weight training. You can get hurt driving a car or lighting a stove but that doesn't mean you should give up driving and cooking — it just means you should be careful with cars and stoves. Injuries don't come out of the blue. You determine whether or not they're going to happen. You have to be careful, pay attention to what you're doing, and, in the event of minor injuries, follow the steps we've outlined for taking care of them. Following the Gold's Gym program will, we hope, result in the physical rewards your body was designed for.

Getting Started

Weight training, like other specialties, has its jargon. We've kept these terms to a minimum, but certain ones are good to know because they're the ones everybody else involved with weight training is familiar with.

A **rep** or **repetition** is a single completed movement of an exercise, from starting position, through the entire movement, then back to the starting position.

A **set** is a prescribed number of repetitions. The length of a set can vary considerably in different programs. In the Gold's Gym weight training program, a set should always be 15 repetitions, except for abdominal exercises or as otherwise noted.

A **circuit** is a prescribed group of exercises performed in rapid succession.

A **barbell** is a long bar with weights at both ends, designed to be used with two hands.

A **dumbbell** is a short bar with weights at either end, designed to be used with one hand.

When we talk about parts of the body like the shoulders or the back, for example, we aren't really being specific enough for weight training. Each part of the body is made up of several different muscles or muscle groups and there are specific exercises for each of them. So, when you are learning a shoulder program, don't let it confuse you when we say one exercise is for the "deltoid" and another for the "trapezius muscles." The anatomical drawings show and name a few key muscles so that you'll have some idea of why you're performing a certain movement and what effect it will have on your body.

We've also used the most common names for our weight-training exercises. This is advantageous because often the name describes both how you do the exercise and the body part to be worked, making it easier to remember.

EQUIPMENT: YOUR BODY

The most valuable item you'll be working with is, of course, your own body. The accompanying drawings will provide the basic anatomical information you're going to need. But there are a few other body facts you might like to know.

There are three major types of muscle tissue in the body. Each type differs in how it is structured, where it is located, how it is activated, and what it does.

Smooth muscle is found in the walls of internal or visceral organs such as blood vessels and intestines. These muscles work automatically, without our conscious control, but they benefit from the general conditioning found in weight training.

Cardiac or heart muscle is a separate type. It becomes stronger through exercise which increases the heart rate. This is a cardiovascular benefit derived from circuit training.

Skeletal muscle is the system of long muscles that control physical movement. This is the type that grows stronger and sometimes larger through progressive resistance exercise.

While general skeletal and muscle structure is the same for everyone — it's obvious that not all bodies are alike and all have different potentials — there is no body that cannot be improved and shaped with weights.

THE BAR NECESSITIES

If you walked into Gold's Gym you'd see hundreds of barbells and dumbbells of assorted sizes, machines with cables and pulleys that exercise all parts of the body, bars to chin yourself on, benches which can be set at various angles for specialized

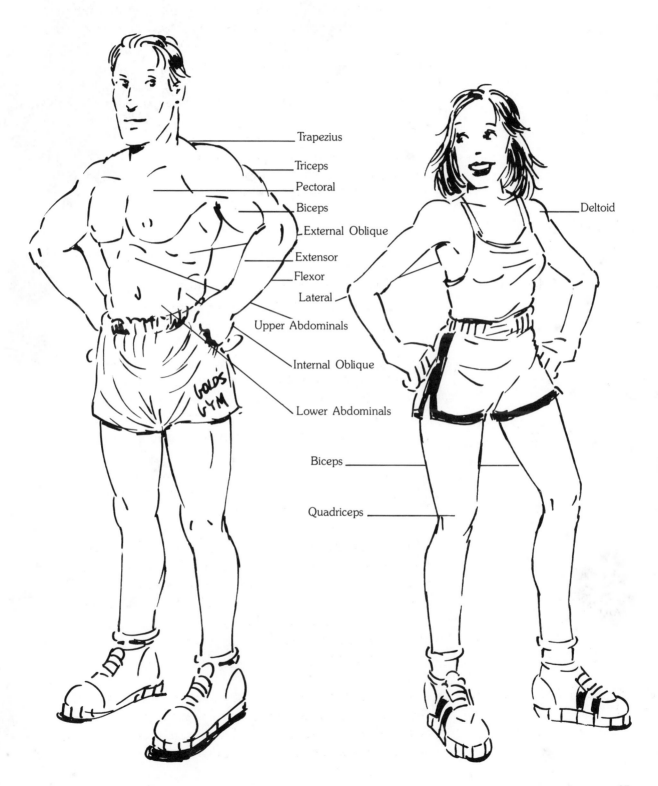

Trapezius

Triceps

Pectoral

Biceps

External Oblique

Extensor

Flexor

Lateral

Upper Abdominals

Internal Oblique

Lower Abdominals

Deltoid

Biceps

Quadriceps

45

movements, and devices to work your calves, abdominals, and so on. Even if you had room for all this equipment in your home, the cost would be prohibitive. That's why we've designed a program of weight training that allows you to duplicate virtually all of the exercises you could do in the gym in the convenience of your own home using a minimum of equipment.

There are three gradations to the Gold's Gym program. In order to get started you'll need only a set of weights, a barbell and two dumbbells. Later on, when you advance to Level III you'll have the option of adding certain pieces of equipment for your exercise routines. However, even at the advanced levels, the number of optional pieces of equipment is minimal.

Olympic weightlifters use a heavy iron bar onto which large iron plates are added. For the Gold's Gym program, however, we recommend the more civilized kind of weight set which can be purchased in almost any sporting goods store at a cost of between $20 and $30.

This type of set consists of
- a long bar, much lighter than that in an Olympic set;
- two short bars; and
- an assortment of plastic-covered weights that fit interchangeably on both the long and the short bars.

It's a great advantage to have a set of weights that has the plates covered with plastic: this helps protect your floors

against scratching and gives you a great deal more leeway in deciding where you're going to exercise.

There are also weights with metal plates that are much smaller than olympic sets. These work well and cost only a little more.

The basic set of weights available to sporting goods stores usually comes with plates totaling about 110 pounds. This should be more than adequate until you reach the advanced stage. When you find you need more weight, you can buy extra plates separately.

Some sets come with 2½ pound plates, while others don't have any smaller than 5 pounds. We recommend you don't buy a set unless it includes 2½ pound plates because the smaller plates allow you to add weight to your exercises more gradually. With 2½ pound plates, you can add 5 pounds to the bar (one 2½ pound plate on each end) while with 5 pound plates, you can't add weight unless you add 10 pounds at a time. That's prohibitively heavy for some exercises.

Since weights don't wear out, a used set is just as useful as a new one. If you'd like to save a little money on equipment, try checking ads in the paper or scouting garage sales. But if you do buy used equipment, there are a couple of things you should watch for:

Make sure you know what kind of set you're buying
You should at least look at a new set in a sporting goods store so you can recognize a similar set. You can buy a different kind if you want to, but it may end up being more awkward to use and too heavy for some of the exercises.

Make sure all the plates and bars in a set are interchangeable
Some manufacturers make bars of different diameters. Check to see that the barbell and dumbbell bars are the same size and that all the weights fit them. If you don't, you will end up having to spend additional money on more plates to complete your set.

Nonadjustable Weights

There are some weights for sale, especially dumbbells, that are one solid piece. We don't recommend buying these kinds of weights because the Gold's Gym Program is based on *pro-*

gressive resistance, being able to add weight to your exercises as you become stronger. With nonadjustable weights, you can't do this — you would need a different set of dumbbells for each weight level in your program. If you already have a set of this kind, however, you can use it for a brief period as you condition yourself for the heart of the Gold's program. We'll explain the set of preprogram conditioning exercises at the end of this chapter.

Making Your Own Weights

Some people, trying to save a little money, attempt to make their own training equipment out of the things they find around the house or garage. We don't think this is a very good idea.

Professional weight sets are balanced, safe and easy to use, designed specifically to be used in a progressive resistance training program. Homemade devices are liable to be unsafe and undependable, awkward to use, and difficult to maneuver in such a way as to do the prescribed movements properly. Using the wrong kind of equipment can lead to a waste of time and effort, and can ultimately be very discouraging.

WHERE TO TRAIN

You can do the Gold's Gym program in your living room, bedroom, garage, or anywhere in your home where you have a few square feet of open space and a mirror in which to watch

yourself. If you can find a place exclusively for weight training, free from distractions, so much the better. Just be sure you have enough room to use the weights without banging into anything. Putting the end of a barbell through your television screen should be avoided.

Another thing to be aware of is that you're going to work up a sweat when you exercise, so it's a good idea to train in an area that has adequate ventilation.

HOW LONG

The Gold's Gym program is designed to take you no more than 15 minutes a day. Using progressive resistance exercises and a P.H.A. system, that is more than enough time for a complete and thorough workout.

WHEN

What time of day you want to set aside for your training workouts is completely up to you. Some people prefer exercising as soon as they wake up. Others like to wait until the end of the day to use their weight training as relaxation and recreation. One problem with training early in the day is that in the beginning you might find yourself fatigued after your 15 minute session. However, once the program begins to take effect, the exercises will leave you refreshed, full of vigor and health, and ready for other activities.

HOW OFTEN

It's important to train frequently enough to maintain your level of conditioning. We recommend five times a week — two days in a row, skip a day, then three days in a row, skip a day, and back to two days in a row. Working out fewer than four times a week, particularly during the first few months of the program, should be avoided. You really need consistency to get the maximum benefits and the maximum feedback, which will be so important in your motivation to continue.

Training more than six times a week, however, isn't a good idea; if you work out too often, you can seriously tire your muscles, which need time to recuperate between workouts. During weeks when you are particularly active, you might want to cut down on the number of weight-training sessions. If, for example, you found yourself playing a few sets of tennis every day, you wouldn't want to train with weights as often as during a week when you were getting little physical activity.

Sometimes you will feel stronger than at other times. If you feel particularly good, try training more often. But if you start tiring and your muscles don't seem to be recuperating well, take it a little bit easier.

If your training schedule has been interrupted for some reason, for example, if you haven't been exercising because of illness, remember it will take you a few days of exercising to get back to your former level. The smart thing to do is ease back into your full schedule gradually, giving your body time to get used to the stress of the exercises again.

But once you start, keep going. Establish the habit of exercise and it will be hard to break. A taste of fitness will carry you on to greater fitness as you feel the pleasure of using your body well.

. . . AND BEFORE YOU START

We've developed the Gold's Gym weight training program primarily to help you look and feel better, but it should also improve your general level of health. To be absolutely certain that you'll get only beneficial results from this program:

Make sure your doctor will let you take up weight training

Weight training is good for certain physical problems, but it can complicate others. If you have cardiac, orthopedic, or other medical problems, check with your doctor before you begin this or any other program of strenuous exercise. Even if you have no reason to think there is anything wrong with you, you should have a medical check-up before undertaking any strenuous physical program.

Be careful not to go too fast

Sometimes it's a temptation to add more weight or additional exercises to your routine before you're really ready. That can be very discouraging in the long run and occasionally dangerous. Take your time. Don't push yourself too hard. You've got the rest of your life to make your body into what you want it to be.

Don't ad-lib the program

We've designed the Gold's Gym program so you'll get maximum results as quickly, and as safely, as possible. We recommend that you don't experiment until you've (at the very least) mastered the routines outlined in this book. By handling weights in the prescribed manner you can avoid strains which might otherwise occur.

PREPROGRAM WEIGHT TRAINING

You may want to prepare for the Gold's Gym Weight Training Program by doing preliminary dumbbell exercises. These are beneficial in themselves and can accustom you to working with weights. The routine works virtually the entire body, but lacks the full range of cardiovascular benefits and muscle toning and shaping derived from the Gold's Gym program. If you have lifted weights before, or if you're confident of your conditioning and anxious to get on with the program, there's no reason why you can't proceed directly to Level I.

Light fixed-weight dumbbells are available today in sporting goods stores, at discount houses, and even in the health departments of some large drug stores. Many people own sets that they have used once or twice and then tucked into the bottom of a closet. Such dumbbells have only limited use, but if you own a pair, you can use them for preprogram conditioning.

Within a week or so, however, you will probably find that working with fixed-weight dumbbells is so easy that in order to get any significant results you will have to spend a lot of time doing a great many repetitions. That's why variable-weight dumbbells are better — by adding weight but doing the same number of repetitions you spend a minimum amount of time exercising.

If you do not now have a set of light fixed-weight dumbbells we suggest that instead of buying those, you spend a few dollars more and purchase a variable-weight dumbbell/barbell system as described earlier.

The seven exercises below can be done with either fixed weights or variable weights; just be certain they aren't so heavy that you become sore or uncomfortable. Variations of these exercises using a barbell instead of a dumbbell appear in other parts of this book.

When you've learned these exercises, try to do at least 15 repetitions of each. If you can't, the dumbbells are probably too heavy for you. Do two complete circuits of the seven exercises without a break.

Shoulder Press Stand upright holding a dumbbell in each hand directly beside your shoulders. Raise the dumbbells straight up over your head until your arms are straight. Turn your palms forward and touch the ends of the dumbbells together lightly. Pause, then bring the weights slowly down to the starting position, palms facing toward each other.

Lateral Raise

Stand holding a dumbbell in each hand, hands at your sides. Slowly lift the dumbbells out to each side, keeping your arms as straight as possible and the palms of your hands turned toward the floor. Raise the weights until they are above the height of your head, pause, then lower them slowly to the starting position.

Knee Bends

Stand holding the dumbbells close to your body at your side. Keeping your back straight, bend your knees and lower your body as far as it will go, raising your heels slightly off the floor. Pause for a moment at the lowest point, then push yourself up to the starting position.

Bent-Over Rowing

Holding a dumbbell in each hand, and keeping your legs straight, bend from the waist until your torso is parallel with the floor. Let your arms hang straight down from the shoulders and hold the dumbbells in a straight line as if they were one continuous bar. Slowly raise the dumbbells until they touch your shoulders, then gradually lower them again to the starting position.

Good Mornings

Stand upright and hold one dumbbell in both hands straight above your head. Slowly bend from the waist until the line of your extended arm is about parallel to the floor. Keep the small of your back as concave as possible. Slowly raise yourself back up to the starting position.

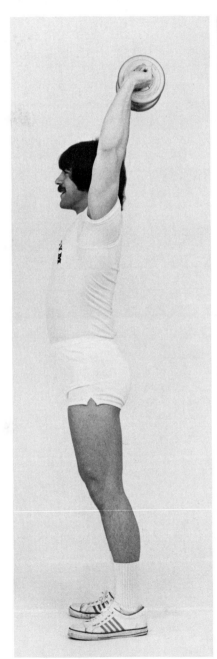

Flys

Lie on your back, your arms out to each side at the shoulders, a dumbbell in each hand, palms up. Keeping your arms straight, lift both of the dumbbells and bring them together until they are directly above your eyes. Slowly lower the weights to the starting position, keeping your arms straight throughout the entire movement.

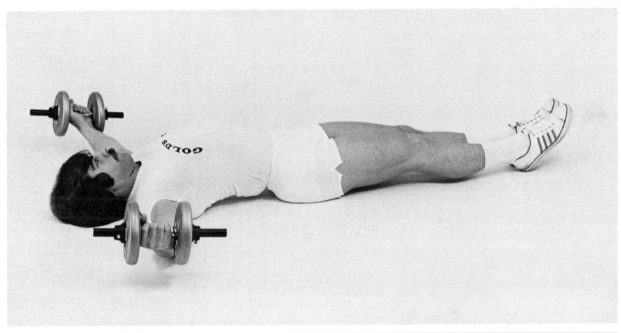

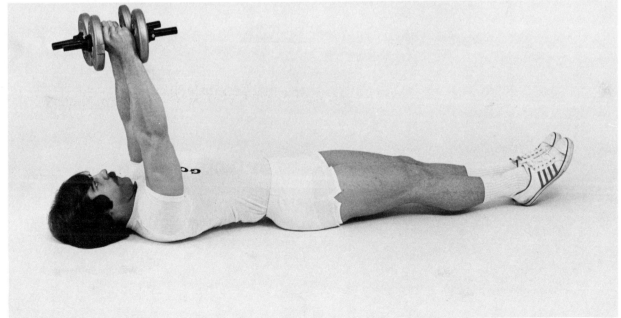

Pullovers

Lie on your back, holding a single dumbbell with both hands at arm's length above your eyes. (Your legs may be straight or bent at the knee.) Keeping your arms straight, gradually lower the weight in an arc so that it touches the floor behind your head. Then raise it slowly to the starting position.

By the time you're able to do the circuit described above without any sense of strain or shortness of breath, you're ready to go on to learn Level I of the Gold's Gym weight-training program.

If you haven't got a weight set as yet, you can continue to benefit by the pre-Level I conditioning program.

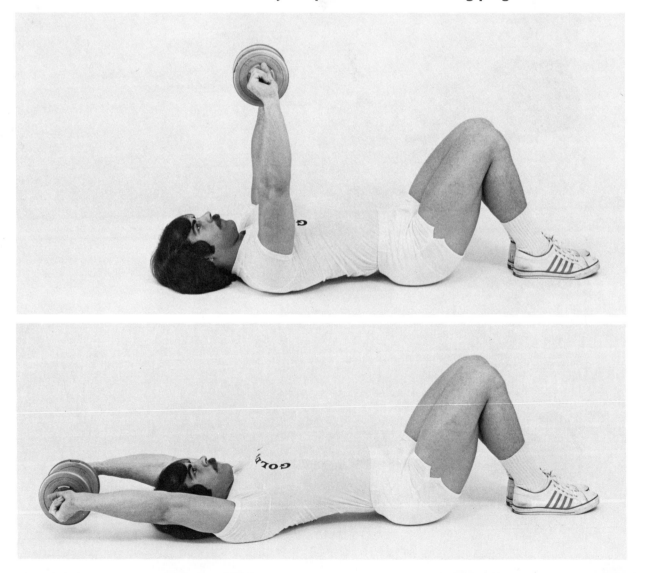

LEVEL I:
Fixed-Weight Training and Conditioning

PURPOSE:

To teach the basic weight training exercises

EQUIPMENT NEEDED:

One barbell with weights

TIME NEEDED:

A maximum of fifteen minutes, four to six times a week

THE FIXED WEIGHT P.H.A. CIRCUIT

As we've already discussed, a circuit of exercises is a series of movements done one right after another without stopping. This kind of training is especially good for cardiovascular conditioning because the continuous movement keeps the heart operating at a level which will strengthen it.

Peripheral Heart Action training is a particular kind of circuit training which works every part of the body. With P.H.A. exercises, you train and "pump" — cause blood to rush through the entire body — while you increase the efficiency of your aerobic and circulatory systems.

The Level I circuit is composed of six barbell exercises (fifteen repetitions each) and one exercise for the abdominal muscles (at least twenty-five repetitions):

Shoulder Press
Upright Rows
Curls
Bent-Over Rows
Front Squats
Deadlifts
Leg Raises

The Level I circuit is the foundation for the exercise programs in all succeeding levels. Once you've learned these movements, you'll continue to use them for as long as you train with weights, so it's very important to learn them correctly now.

Weight and Repetitions

All barbell exercises in Level I are done with a fixed amount of weight on the bar. Because each of the seven exercises works a different part of the body, and your muscles vary in strength, you'll find some of the exercises easier to do than others.

To determine what weight is right for you, find the maximum amount of weight that allows you to do fifteen repetitions of the exercise you find *most difficult*, then use that amount for the whole circuit. Judging by our experience this will probably be the Shoulder Press or Curls.

If you've chosen a weight that allows you to do fifteen repetitions of each exercise, but tires you so much that you can't get through the circuit, switch to a lighter weight until you improve your general conditioning. However, if you have trouble completing a circuit with even the lightest amount of weight, or you have trouble doing the exercise exactly as the instructions indicate, try the circuit just using the bar itself. Then, when you've done a few circuits this way, you can begin to add small amounts of weight. This gradual approach is one of the benefits of progressive resistance.

How Many Circuits?

Your ultimate goal in Level I will be to do four circuits without stopping. When you're starting out, you'll probably be able to do only one or two. If you can do three or four right away, you probably aren't using enough weight to effectively train your muscles. Increase the weight and cut down on the number of circuits. Use an amount of weight that challenges but doesn't overwhelm you, then give yourself time to build up enough endurance to do four circuits.

Once you've reached that goal, it's time to increase the weight. When you do this you may find that, as before, you can't get through all four circuits. Do as many as you can and when you find yourself unable to go on, stop and take off some of the weight. Do the remaining circuits until you have finished four. Whenever you add weight to the bar, you'll know it's too much if you can't do at least two complete circuits with the new amount.

You may wonder how many times to add weight to the barbells before you go on to the variable-weight program in Level II. It's truly up to you — the essence of the Gold's Gym program is that you tailor it to fit your own needs and capabilities. It all depends on how your muscles respond. Following the exercises, we'll discuss three criteria that will help you decide when it's time to move up to Level II.

SHOULDER PRESS

Body Parts Worked: Shoulders and Triceps (back of arm)

Benefits

For a man the shoulder press will add breadth to the shoulders, making the waist appear slimmer. For women the shoulder press will be especially valuable in firming and trimming the upper arms and shoulders. It also works the triceps, an area of the body that usually begins to sag with age and neglect.

Women should recognize that any exercise dealing with the upper body is probably more difficult for them than it is for men as it is rare for a woman to have developed much upper-body strength. But take heart; this means you'll probably make greater relative progress than a man doing the same exercise.

Before you begin your first barbell exercise, there is one important rule you should know to keep your balance and protect the lower back from strain. Unless we tell you otherwise, always bend your knees when lifting a weight from the floor or when putting it down.

The Exercise

Although we have numbered the steps for clarity in learning, you should do the exercises as one continuous movement.

Position

With the barbell on the floor, stand with your feet comfortably apart (about sixteen inches). Bend your knees slightly and grasp the bar with an overhand grip, hands a little wider apart than shoulder-width. Straighten up and swing the weight to shoulder level, then tuck your elbows in so the bar is held steady just below the chin, touching the upper chest, elbows slightly forward. (This movement is called "cleaning" the weight.)

The Exercise

1. Lift the bar straight over your head until your arms are fully extended.
2. Pause for a moment on top.
3. Slowly lower the bar until it has returned to the starting shoulder position.

Caution

To avoid losing control of the weight on top, concentrate on your balance by making sure of your foot placement and keeping your hips tight.

UPRIGHT ROWS

Body Parts Worked: Shoulders
Trapezius (muscles between neck and shoulder)
Biceps

Benefits

Upright Rows are very good for working the entire upper body. Men will find it really contributes to a wide-shouldered look as well as broadening the back. For women, it's essential for developing upper-body strength and firmness. It stretches the back to help eliminate flab, and firms and shapes the bicep.

Position

With the weight on the floor and your feet comfortably apart, bend at the knees and grasp the bar with an overhand grip, hands about six inches apart. Straighten up and let the bar hang in front of you, arms fully extended, knuckles toward the floor.

The Exercise

1. Keeping your hands close to your body, lift the bar to a point just below your chin. Your elbows should be pointed up and out and be higher than the bar.
2. Stop for a moment on top.
3. Lower the bar slowly until your arms are fully extended once more and you have returned to the starting position.

Caution

There is a tendency to make upright rows easier by swinging the bar up and out instead of lifting it straight up. If you do it that way, you're simply not going to get what this exercise has to offer.

CURLS

Body Part Worked: Biceps

Benefits

This is one of the most popular of all weight training exercises. Men like it because it gives the appearance and produces the reality of strength to the arm. Women like it because it shapes the arms and helps them develop the strength in an area in which few women have it. In addition, of course, any arm exercise is especially beneficial for most sports activities.

Position

With your feet comfortably apart and knees bent, grasp the bar with an underhand grip, hands about shoulder width apart. Straighten up with the weight hanging down in front of you, arms fully extended. Keep your elbows tucked in against your body and well forward, the inside of your forearms facing straight ahead. Throughout the movement your elbows stay in the same position, acting as a pivot.

The Exercise

1. Keeping your elbows stationary, slowly lift up the weight in an arc until it is between your chin and upper chest.
2. Pause for a moment.
3. Slowly let the weight down until your arms are fully extended.

Tip

To help you derive more benefit from the exercise, when you get to the top of the arc, "cramp" the arm muscles slightly. This "making a muscle" helps shape the arm.

Caution

As you do each repetition, make sure that you're lifting with your arms, not your shoulders. Lowering the weight is as much a part of the exercise as lifting it. Keep control of the weight; don't let it drop. A common mistake to avoid is swinging the weight up instead of lifting it in a controlled manner.

 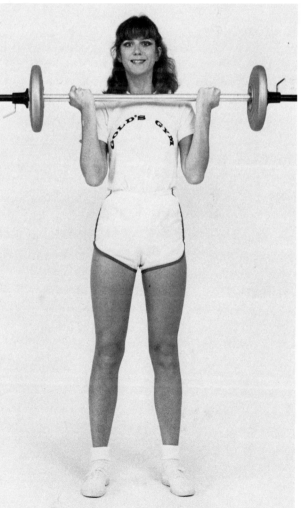

BENT-OVER ROWS

Body Part Worked: Back (laterals)

Benefits

This exercise is designed to broaden the back. It contributes to upper-body strength. In women it is especially helpful in developing a back that looks well-shaped in a bathing suit or a backless dress.

It's also beneficial for overall back health. When you strengthen and condition the muscles of the back, there is far less chance of developing lower back pain, a slipped disc, or any of the other common back complaints.

With this exercise you begin to engage some of the larger muscles of the body, so the weight will be easier to lift. That's good news because by this point in the circuit you'll probably be starting to get a little bit tired.

Position

With feet comfortably apart, bend down and grasp the bar with an overhand grip, hands a little wider apart than shoulder width. Keeping your torso bent over so that it remains almost parallel to the floor, lift the weight by straightening your legs until your knees are just slightly flexed. Let the weight hang straight down at arm's length.

The Exercise

1. Keeping your body in the same bent-over position, slowly lift the bar straight up until it touches your chest. As you lift, gently squeeze the muscles of the back together.
2. Pause for a moment.
3. Slowly lower the bar, keeping it fully under control at all times, until your arms are once more fully extended.

Caution

Keep your knees slightly flexed rather than locked during this exercise; that way, no matter how heavy a weight you use, there is little chance of losing balance and straining your back.

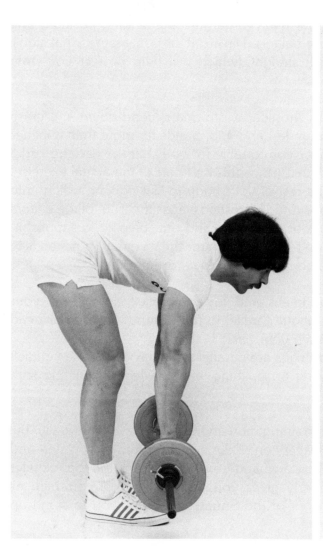

FRONT SQUATS

Benefits

Body Parts Worked: Legs and hips

Both men and women often complain that as time passes the sides of their hips and backs of their thighs look more and more like cottage cheese. This exercise is designed to take care of those complaints. Squats are a good basic exercise for the legs but the movement is also very good for toning and strengthening the entire lower body, the buttocks, abdominals and lower back.

There are two kinds of Squats: those performed with the bar held in front of the body and those done with the weight resting on the shoulders behind the neck. We recommend Front Squats to anyone training at home: you don't have to lift the bar over your head to get into the starting position, and keeping the bar balanced in front of you assures that you'll keep your back straight (which will help protect you from injury).

Position

With feet about shoulder-width apart, bend down and grasp the bar with an underhand grip, hands no more than 8 inches apart, closer if it's comfortable for you. Lift the bar and curl it up under your chin (since this isn't part of the actual exercise, you can use the rest of your body to "swing" the weight into place). The bar should be resting across the front of the deltoid muscles, with your elbows up and out, helping to support it. Your hands don't hold the bar up; their primary function is to keep it in place by pressing it toward the body.

The Exercise

1. Bend your knees and lower yourself down until your thighs are just about parallel to the ground. Keep your head up and don't arch your back.
2. Once your thighs are parallel to the ground, raise yourself up, concentrating on pushing with the legs, not lifting with the back.

Tip

In most weight training movements you breathe naturally, but Squats are an exception. Take a deep breath as you start and hold it as you go down and up. As you reach the top, exhale. Breathing properly gives you just a little more strength as you're coming out of the Squat, and helps you to stand up again.

This exercise is simply a "deep knee bend" with weight added, but because of that extra weight (which raises your center of gravity), you have to be much more careful to keep your balance. As you lower yourself, don't "bounce" at the bottom; stay fully under control. Later, when you are using a heavier weight, this control could really make a difference in preventing injury.

DEADLIFTS

Body Parts Worked: Back, Legs, Entire Body

Benefits

Deadlifts are the single most beneficial exercise you can do. They're helpful for overall flexibility, working both the upper and lower body simultaneously. You may find it a novel experience to do an exercise in which you actually use the whole body, as most of us aren't accustomed to using more than a few body parts at one time.

Deadlifts seem to be a very natural movement, but be careful to concentrate on technique so you don't pick up any wrong habits. You will eventually do this exercise with a great deal more weight than you're using at present, so now is the time to master technique.

Position

Stand with your toes under the bar. Your feet should be as far apart as necessary for a good, firm stance. Grasp the bar with one hand overhand, the other hand underhand. This grip will help keep the bar from rolling out of your hand. Your hands should be a little wider apart than shoulder width, wider than the stance of your feet.

The Exercise

1. With the weight hanging at arm's length, stand up, *straightening your knees and back at the same time.* Use legs and back to distribute the stress.
2. As you come to a full-standing position, put your shoulders back a little as if standing at attention. This guarantees the proper completion of the movement.
3. Reverse the process to put the weight down, using your legs and back to lower the bar.
4. Touch the weight to the floor.

Caution

Don't let the fact that the weight seems so light cause you to use sloppy technique. Using both the legs and back to control the bar will become increasingly important as you start to deal with more weight. Since you are now near the end of the circuit and may be getting tired, additional concentration may be needed to be certain that you are doing each movement properly.

LEG RAISES

Body Part Worked: Lower abdominals

Benefits

The most underworked muscles in the whole body are the abdominals which all body builders abbreviate to "abs". Although everyone is aware of the fact that they are important to the look of the torso, most people don't know that they also help hold many internal organs in place and play an important part in various physiological functions.

Additionally, your abs provide strength in other ways you may not be aware of. The ab muscles have a lot to do with the power you can generate for many sports actions such as serving a tennis ball, swinging a golf club, etc. More specific information on the special value of specific exercise and sports appears in Chapter 8.

There are two sets of ab muscles, upper and lower. Leg Raises are designed to work the lower, which will help avoid the sag that frequently shows below the belt. In Chapter 9, Advanced Body Shaping, we'll tell you about Crunches, which tighten the upper ab muscles.

You have been doing fifteen repetitions per circuit for the barbell exercises, but for the Leg Raises, try to work up to twenty-five as you get into shape.

Position

Lie on your back on the floor, or on a table or bench. If you are using a table or bench, lie with your buttocks right at the end, your legs extended without support. Tuck your hands, palms down, under your buttocks. If your hands feel pinched under your weight, try moving them slightly forward or back until they're comfortable. Doing Leg Raises on the floor, you will begin and end in a horizontal position; however, if you are on a raised surface, you will be able to lower your legs below the level of the rest of the body.

The Exercise

1. Slowly raise both legs simultaneously, keeping them straight, with knees locked, until they are pointed directly overhead, or as close as you can come to it.
2. Lower them, moving slowly and under control, back to the starting position.

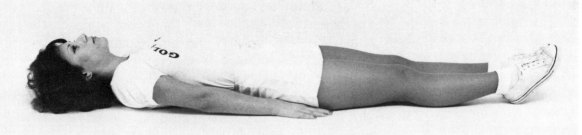

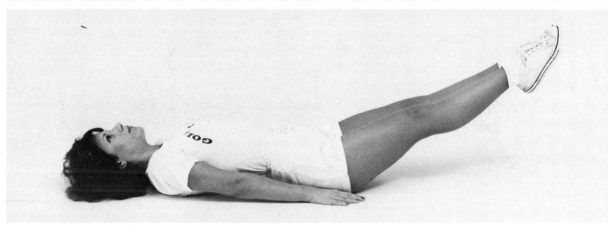

Bent-Leg Raises

What determines the difficulty of Leg Raises is how straight you keep your legs. If you find that you cannot do the exercise with your legs straight, the alternative is Bent-Leg Raises. These are done almost exactly the same way, except that as you raise your legs, you bend your knees. The more you bend your knees, the easier the exercise becomes. As you progress and become stronger, you'll be able to straighten your legs more and more.

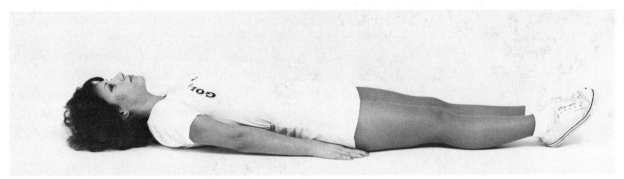

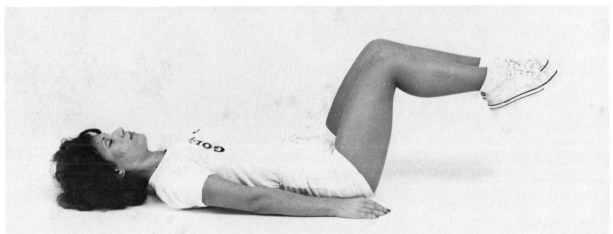

BACK WHERE WE STARTED . . .

When you have finished Leg Raises, you have completed one circuit. In the first few sessions, one circuit may be your limit. But very soon, you will be in condition to do more.

When you do more than one circuit at a time, return to the Shoulder Press as soon as you have finished Leg Raises. You may feel out of breath, but your shoulders will have had plenty of rest since you started the circuit. To get the full benefit of the Peripheral Heart Action Program you have to keep going.

Remember, when it gets to the point where you can do four circuits with comfort, it's time to add more weight or go on to the next level.

When to Move On

You will have to decide for yourself when it's time to move on to Level II. But, to help you decide, here are a few criteria for judging when you are ready:

You will be noticeably stronger

You should be able to tell that your muscles are in much better condition, better toned.

You will have better endurance

Being out of breath is really not a good way to tell how hard you've worked. The P.H.A. circuit is designed to keep you out of breath a lot of the time. Endurance really means being able to continue even though you're tired, being able to work through initial fatigue.

You will be eager for further challenge

By now, working through a fixed-weight circuit should feel natural. At Level II you'll be doing the same exercises, but with heavier weights and, therefore, greater difficulty. This is part of the *progressive* nature of the training that is going to contribute to changing the shape and feel of your body. If you feel stronger, have the endurance, and want the challenge, you're ready for Level II.

LEVEL II: Variable-Weight Training and Body Shaping

PURPOSE:

To begin to shape your body and to continue toning and strengthening your muscles

EQUIPMENT NEEDED:

One barbell with weights

TIME NEEDED:

A maximum of fifteen minutes, four to six times a week

THE SHAPE OF THINGS TO COME

At Level II, along with an increase in strength, you'll begin to actually **see** a change in the look of your body — muscles that are used and conditioned **look different** from those that aren't.

Level I used a fixed amount of weight for the whole circuit; it was more important at that point to develop your overall conditioning, tone up the muscles, and learn to handle the weights than to put a lot of stress on your muscles, which weren't really ready for it anyway. As you worked through Level I, you certainly noticed that some parts of your body are stronger than others. In Level II, we will show you how to modify your program to compensate for these differences in muscular strength. Using different weights for different muscles is essential for the shaping process which comes about not just by using a muscle but by overloading it; that is, giving it more weight than it can easily handle. But because some muscles are stronger than others, weight that is heavy enough to overload one may be too light for another.

For example, the same weight feels a lot heavier when you're doing a Shoulder Press than when you do a Deadlift or

Squat, because for most people the legs and back are a lot stronger than the arms and shoulders. The only way you can get maximum shaping of each body part is by tailoring the resistance to the strength of that part. In other words, use more weight when you exercise the stronger parts and less when you work the smaller muscle groups. Variable-weight training is what's called for now.

The circuit of exercises in Level II is the same one you learned in Level I. In fact, you'll be using the same exercises throughout the Gold's Gym program, adding others we'll show you later for the special shaping and strengthening you want. But now these movements will feel different because you'll be adding weight to many of them. Again, when your strength increases and the exercise gets too easy for you, add a little more weight for that particular exercise. This keeps you training with progressive resistance.

It's important to remember, no matter how much or how little weight you use in your routine, that movements should always be performed in a constant, rapid fashion without time out to rest. In that way you will continue to develop a high level of cardiovascular fitness.

If you find you can't get through the program without resting, you're probably using too much weight. Keep in mind the difference between weight training and weightlifting and don't let your pride hinge on how much weight you can pick up. Shape, strength and health are your goals, not setting weight-lifting records.

KEEPING TRACK

If you haven't already begun to fill out your exercise chart on page 23, you've missed some of the satisfaction of comparing yourself before and after. But the major improvements are yet to come, so start charting your progress now.

To show you about how much weight a typical trainer might add to an exercise, we've included sample charts of a man and a woman at Level II of Gold's Gym program. Rate of progress is an individual matter — don't be concerned if your chart doesn't match either of these.

HOW TO DO THE CIRCUIT

Use the same exercises you learned in Level I, but alter the amount of weight you use for each exercise, depending on how difficult it is for you. You should use enough weight to

GOLD'S TRAINING ROUTINE		John					LEG RAISES	
LEVEL II	DATE	WT.	DATE	WT.	DATE	WT.		
1. Shoulder Press	3/10	25	3/26	30			DATE	NO.
2. Upright Rows		25		25			3/10	25
3. Curls		30		30			3/18	30
4. Bent Over Rows		40		45			4/9	40
5. Squats		45		50			4/20	50
6. Dead Lifts		50		55				
7.								
8.								
9.								

GOLD'S TRAINING ROUTINE		Jane					LEG RAISES	
LEVEL II	DATE	WT.	DATE	WT.	DATE	WT.		
1. Shoulder Press	3/10	15	3/26	20			DATE	NO.
2. Upright Rows		15		15			3/4	15
3. Curls		20		20			3/14	20
4. Bent Over Rows		30		35			3/29	30
5. Squats		35		40			4/22	40
6. Dead Lifts		40		45			4/29	50
7.								
8.								
9.								

make each exercise challenging but not too much to prevent you from getting through the entire program.

Throughout the remainder of the Gold's Gym program you should do no more than **fifteen repetitions** of any exercise for which you use weights. You may do more repetitions for those exercises that do not involve weights, such as Leg Raises, Sit-Ups, and others.

We recommend you perform a minimum of twenty-five Leg Raises at first and then try to add an additional repetition each day. This way you can work up to fifty in little more than a month.

How Many Circuits?

The program becomes a lot more demanding when you start using heavier weights. So, for Level II, your routine will consist of only **two** circuits. If you find you can't get through two circuits, use a little less weight. If it seems too easy, then add some.

When you feel you have mastered Level I and Level II, it's time to design your own circuit, adding new exercises to help you shape your body the way you want it, while maintaining general conditioning and tone. Level III, Advanced Body Shaping, will show you how.

Adjusting the Weight

Most weight sets use collars with screw adjustments to hold the weights securely on the bar. At first removing and then replacing these collars every time you change the amount of weight needed for an exercise is time consuming, but you'll find you get a lot faster with practice. Some people prefer to put the minimum weight they'll need for a workout inside the collar and then slip additional weights on outside as needed. On many weight sets the fit is tight enough so that you can do your routine without the weights slipping off, however, we cannot recommend that you do this if there is any chance at all the weight could come loose and damage you or your training area. Certainly, whenever you are working with dumbbells, you should never attempt to use them without the plates held firmly in place by the collars.

LEVEL III:
Advanced Body Shaping

PURPOSE: To shape and strengthen particular body areas

EQUIPMENT NEEDED: One barbell, two dumbbells, and weights. For some exercises, a partner or special equipment

TIME NEEDED: 15 minutes, four to six times a week

YOU START WITH YOURSELF

Any advanced body shaping program you undertake must be suited to your own unique characteristics. You may be long- or short-waisted, have naturally great legs or be a bit knock-kneed . . . tend to put on weight easily or be able to eat anything without gaining an ounce. You may be wide in the shoulders or narrow . . . have long upper arms and short forearms or the reverse . . . be strong or weak, tall or short, large in the rear or small — or any combination of the above.

We don't know what your body looks like or how you'd like to change it, so we can't tell you what your personal program ought to be. But we can help you design a program to suit your desires, show you how to vary the basic circuit of exercises so that you choose your own priorities, and decide where to concentrate your energy.

Expanding the Circuit

When we take up any new pursuit, most of us start out with a pretty good idea of what we want and where we're going and then find that our actual experience dramatically alters our original goals. Sometimes we decide to get more involved than we thought we would. We want more. That can happen with weight training.

Looking into a mirror and seeing the visible effects of systematic weight training can be exhilarating. Your body is no longer a passive object, something you're just "stuck with." Now it's under your control. For a lot of people, that's sufficient. It's why they started weight training in the first place, and they're completely satisfied to continue their programs as they've learned them in order to maintain their nice new body shapes. But others get so turned on by the changes they see that they want to see more of them. They're willing to put in a little more time and effort, perhaps add a few more exercises to their routines.

You may be one of those people, or you may just want a little more variety, a few more options to spice up your own program. In either case, we'd like to give you a little information on how to expand your personal weight-training program.

ADVANCED CIRCUIT PLANNING

Once you've mastered the necessary Level III exercises, you can slowly add them to your basic routine. Try all the new exercises over a period of time before you settle on a favorite. In this manner you can create a wide variety of circuits. Remember, each movement does something different to your body. They're all unique. Some of the new ones depend on the use of special equipment and a number are best done with the help of a workout partner.

Many people wonder if they should add more circuits as they get more advanced in weight training. It isn't really necessary. What counts is the number of exercises you do. By the time you begin adding two or three more exercises to your circuits you'll be doing the *equivalent* of an extra circuit. How you organize those exercises is up to you. If it helps your planning to divide your routine into three separate circuits instead of putting everything together into two, that's fine. The important thing is to keep training as continuously as possible so you get the full amount of benefit from the P.H.A. aspects of the program.

Many people at the Gym train their abdominals separately from the rest of their body. The advantage is that you can spend as much time working on your waistline as you want without slowing down and interrupting your rapid, circuit-training routines. There are a number of ways you can do this: you can concentrate on the abs and train them either before or after you do your weight training circuits, or you can do the exercises for the waistline at a different time of the day. Whatever your choice, four ab exercises should be done in a continuous manner, like the rest of your exercising.

A Matter of Priorities

The first thing to do in Level III is learn the new exercises (indicated by **bold face** type). They're organized according to body part and we indicate how they affect each muscle or muscle group. Once you've tried all the exercises a few times go ahead and design your own circuit, putting a routine together according to how you feel about your body and what you want to do with it. Each of the circuits we propose includes exercises for other parts of the body so you'll continue to keep up your general conditioning while you specialize in shaping those parts most important to you.

It's best to begin by working all the body parts in rotation, shoulders one time, chest the next and so on until you have learned the exercises for your entire body. After you've done this, you can vary the rotation to concentrate on the parts of the body you think need the most work. If your shoulders are what you're concerned about, for example, you can follow your Advanced Shoulder Program every other workout, every third workout or whenever you see fit. After a while, you can adapt your program to reflect the changes you've observed in the shape and proportion of your physique. It doesn't happen overnight but it won't take long, either.

HOW TO DESIGN YOU OWN BODY PARTS PROGRAM

All the Advanced Body Shaping, Level III, exercises have been divided into two groups: basic and supplementary. Concentrate on mastering the basic exercises first and, when you're comfortable with those, go on and learn the movements in the supplementary group. Supplementary exercises are indicated by brackets.

For example, in the Advanced Chest Program, the push-ups, dumbell press, and dumbbell flys are basic; the bench press, incline/decline press, and pullovers are supplementary.

Let's assume, for example, that you want to design a circuit that concentrates on the chest. To start, you have the basic circuit:

Shoulder Press
Upright Rows
Curls
Bent-Over Rows
Squats
Deadlifts

(We've left out the Leg Raises because we'll be dealing with abdominal exercises separately.)
The Advanced Chest Program contains six new exercises—three basic and three supplementary:

Push-Ups
Dumbbell Press
Dumbbell Flys
[Bench Press]
[Incline/Decline Press]
[Pullovers]

Let's say you want to add the basic exercises to your original circuit. Now you'll have a routine with nine exercises. Below is one possible routine for accenting the chest.

Shoulder Press (shoulders)
Push-Ups (chest)
Upright Rows (shoulders)
Curls (biceps)
Dumbbell Press (chest)
Bent-Over Rows (back)
Squats (lower body)
Dumbbell Flys (chest)
Deadlifts (legs and back)

Keep exercises for a specific body part sequenced between exercises for other body parts, so that you have a chance to rest. It's not an iron-clad rule — sometimes planning routines this way just gets too complicated.

Variations on a Theme	In Level III you should do two complete circuits per workout. But there are several different ways you can put these circuits together:

Instead of adding *all* of the new body-part exercises to each circuit, you can put some of them in the first circuit, others in the second. This will give you fewer exercises in each of the circuits and make your routine a little less demanding.

Instead of just specializing in one body part, you can work two of them. To do this, simply combine one complete circuit accenting one of the body parts with a second circuit emphasizing another.

It is a good idea to plan your workouts so that you don't emphasize the same body part two days in a row. You can specialize in a certain body part two sessions in a row as long as you've had at least one day of rest in between.

Abdominal Exercises

The waist is one area of the body that everybody is interested in firming up. Because there are two different areas of abs — upper and lower — for real results just one kind of exercise isn't enough. And there are other exercises which contribute to the narrow waist and flat stomach we'd all like to have.

To fully exercise the abdominal area we will use the following movements (the last three are **new**):

Leg Raises
Crunches
Bent-Legged Sit-Ups
Twists

You can include the ab exercises in your circuits by adding the first two to the end of the first circuit, and the last two to the end of the second circuit. This would make the Chest Program we've already developed look like this:

FIRST CIRCUIT	**SECOND CIRCUIT**
Shoulder Press	Shoulder Press
Push-Ups	**Push-Ups**

Upright Rows | Upright Rows
Curls | Curls
Dumbbell Press | **Dumbbell Press**
Bent-Over Rows | Bent-Over Rows
Squats | Squats
Dumbbell Flys | **Dumbbell Flys**
Deadlifts | Deadlifts
Leg Raises | **Bent-Legged Sit-Ups**
Crunches | **Twists**

If you were to decide to work two body parts during the same workout — chest and arms, for example — you would need to design two *different* circuits, adding exercises from the Chest Program to one, and exercises from the Arm Program to the other:

FIRST CIRCUIT – Chest | **SECOND CIRCUIT – Arms**
Shoulder Press | **Shoulder Press**
Push-Ups | **Tricep Curls**
Upright Rows | Upright Rows
Curls | Curls
Dumbbell Press | Bent-Over Rows
Bent-Over Rows | Squats
Squats | **Wrist Curls**
Dumbbell Flys | Deadlifts
Deadlifts | **Bent-Legged Sit-Ups**
Leg Raises | **Twists**
Crunches |

Too Much of a Good Thing

There is a cartoon on the bulletin board at the Gym that shows a mailman at the door of a house. He's holding a package labeled "Leg Program." A man with huge shoulders, chest and arms but with skinny, pipe-stemmed legs stands in the doorway. "Thanks," says the man, with a look of relief on his face. "I've been waiting for this."

As you get more involved in the program and begin to concentrate on certain body parts, don't forget that the body is really one system and talking about "body parts" is really a kind of fiction. All of the parts are connected, so don't let yourself get so caught up with your problem areas that you neglect the remainder of your body. Shape and firmness are great to have, but as those Greek statues prove to us, balance and proportion are essential for good looks.

A FRIEND IN NEED

There are certain exercises in the following pages that can be done only with the help of a partner if you don't have certain specialized equipment. But even for the regular barbell and dumbbell exercises, there are ways a partner can help you get more out of the movement.

"Spotting" is standing by to help in case someone else has trouble. In an exercise like the Bench Press it's possible to let the weight down onto your chest and not be able to lift it off again. A partner spots by standing nearby in case you need a little help raising it up. With Squats, a partner would be ready to lend a hand with balance or with the weight.

It's always reassuring to have somebody spotting for you. It lets you go ahead and attempt to lift as heavy a weight as you want without any fear that it might get away from you.

"Forcing" Reps

"Forcing" reps is a technique for getting the fullest effort from your body. After you've done as many repetitions as possible, your partner gives you just a small amount of help, enabling you to lift the weight two or three more times. For instance, if you were doing a Shoulder Press, you would choose an amount of weight that you could lift 12 times and, as you got to the 13th rep, your partner would put a finger under the bar and help you "force" three more repetitions. This technique is very beneficial because you're certain to get all the overload your muscles can handle.

Sharing your weight-training sessions can be fun, but there are certain guidelines that should be observed:

Add energy to the workout, don't take it away. You should help your partner "psych up," not be the cause of his distraction. Keeping your partner focused on the exercise will help avoid accidents.

Use competition as a way of encouraging rather than discouraging each other. Some people are stronger than others so two workout partners shouldn't really be in competition with each other as to how much weight they can lift or how many exercises they can do. A few words of encouragement during the last few reps of any exercise can be a big help to the person who is doing it.

Agree to watch each other's technique and keep each other honest. Even when you're working out with a partner, you're still training your own body, but having someone else there is good in case you get sloppy with your technique and start to "cheat." It's not a matter of being critical. Try to act as each other's "mirror" and point out how your partner might do the exercise better.

Working with a partner has a lot of other benefits. When you have somebody else counting on you to exercise at a particular time, you're less liable to skip training sessions. And, aside from the encouragement you get, you also have somebody with whom you can share the expense of the equipment.

ABOUT EQUIPMENT

If a set of dumbbells didn't come with your weight set, get some now to do the Level III exercises. Being able to work the sides of the body independently of one another will give you the ability to do many additional exercises.

When it comes to dumbbells, it's even more important to have 2½ pound plates. You'll be lifting a dumbbell with only one hand and a very small difference in weight can be crucial. You'll find that most weight sets give you a small wrench (like but using a small open-ended or box wrench will get the job done faster.

Optional Equipment

There's a lot of exercise equipment on the market, stuff with shiny chrome whatchamacallits, natural wood-grained whozits, rack and pinion gizmos and torsion steel thingamabobs. Many people claim they have some miracle system, pill or piece of equipment that will make you physically fit and give you a marvelous body shape with practically no effort on your part. Those claims are just hot air. It would be nice if we could get the full benefit of exercise without expending energy on training — getting something for nothing, in other words — but that just doesn't happen.

When you are first starting out, almost *any* kind of exercise is beneficial and certainly a whole lot better than none at all. But some shiny device that offers you a fixed-tension spring as resistance is only going to help for a little while, because that resistance must get progressively greater as you get stronger if you want to keep making progress.

Additionally, these machines usually work only certain body parts in certain ways — which won't give you full body-shaping benefit — and they don't necessarily give you any cardiovascular conditioning. We know someone who spent over $300 on a "home gym" which consisted of a platform and weights sliding along a slanted track. You sit or lie on the platform and push or pull yourself along the track and the weights provide variable resistance. There's nothing you can do with that machine that we can't duplicate with our basic set of weights. And you can do additional movements with a barbell and dumbbells that you can't do on that kind of machine.

Machines *can* be useful in training the body — Gold's Gym is full of them. There are arm and leg machines, devices with weights, pulleys and variable-resistance leverage design. But there are also a lot of barbells and dumbbells, and they get a lot of use. So if you want maximum benefit in minimum time, don't get sidetracked by the equipment salesmen. We think you'll make a lot more progress with the Gold's Gym program and the equipment we recommend than with most of the inefficient devices you commonly see in many stores. Sticking with the basics will save you time, energy, and money.

On the Other Hand . . .

There are some pieces of equipment that you can use in conjunction with barbells and dumbbells to add a greater variety of exercises to your routines and to make certain movements a lot easier. You can do a very effective program without it; but this equipment gives you more ways to shape the body and helps you increase the efficiency of certain movements.

For instance, there are a number of exercises in the Advanced Body Shaping Program that require or are made easier by a bench, slant board, or chinning bar. Each piece of equipment has its special uses.

Basic Bench

The basic bench is just that: something like a padded piano bench but stronger. Movements like the Dumbbell Press and Flys are much better done on a bench because they require you to drop your arms and the weights lower than your body. You can use any kind of bench for this, providing it can hold your weight and won't tip over. If you decide to buy the kind made especially for weight training, don't forget there are some bargains on the used market.

Bench Press Bench

This is a bench with a couple of upright supports at one end across which you can rest a barbell. You use this for doing Bench Presses, which are a kind of upside-down Push-Ups. Without the rack, you need somebody to hand you the weight after you lie down and take it from you when you're finished. This exercise requires too much weight for you to get in position any other way.

This type of bench is also useful for exercises requiring a basic bench, so you might consider getting this one right away instead of buying the simpler one and then spending more money when you decide you want to do Bench Presses.

Incline and/or Decline Bench

You can adjust some benches so that you lie on a slant, either declined (head lower than hips) or inclined (head higher than hips). If you do Bench Presses on an incline you concentrate your efforts on the upper part of the chest while decline Bench Presses work the lower. If you come across a bench that is both adjustable and has a rack for Bench Presses, you'll have everything you need all in one.

Slant Board

When you do Sit-Ups on an angle with your feet higher than your hips, you increase the amount of effort needed to do the exercise. This kind of increased effort is a form of progressive resistance and helps to get your stomach muscles in tip-top shape.

There are two kinds of slant boards. The first is just that: a board that has a strap at one end into which you put your feet; you prop it up on a piece of furniture or some other support and you lie head-down to do your regular Bent-Legged Sit-Ups. Actually, if you're good with tools, you can make it pretty easily. Just make sure the straps are secure and the board is firm enough to take your weight.

Sporting goods stores sell a more sophisticated version, a folding bench that you can carry like a suitcase but which opens up to be a self-supporting slant board that can be adjusted to various angles. You can do your Sit-Ups on this and Leg Raises as well. They sell for as little as $20 in some places, but a word of caution: make sure when you get one that it's strong enough to hold your weight. It might be better in the long run to spend a little more and get a stronger, better quality board.

Chinning Bar

Chins are a great exercise but difficult to do without a chinning bar. You can get an adjustable chinning bar at most sporting goods stores and they aren't very expensive. This kind of bar consists of an adjustable length of tubing with rubber tips at each end which you can put across a doorway and tighten so that it will hold your weight.

There are only two things to be concerned about when you put your bar in the doorway:

Make sure it's tight enough to hold you. Otherwise you might suddenly find yourself in free-fall.

Check to see that the wood of the door jamb is strong enough to hold you and the bar.

You can go out and buy all the weight-training equipment in the world. If you want a device to strengthen your grip or weights to fasten around your ankles, go ahead. Just consider two questions: can I get the same results with my basic equipment, and will the energy I devote to using other kinds of equipment keep me from working as hard as I should on my own weight-training program? If the answers to both these questions are "no," and you're really enthusiastic about a particular device or piece of equipment, buy it. That's what money's for. Besides, it might even have a shiny chrome whatchamacallit, a natural wood-grained whozit and come with a 400mm zoom lens!

Advanced Chest Program

Push-Ups
Dumbbell Press
Dumbbell Flys
[Bench Press]
[Incline/Decline Press]
[Pullovers]

BENEFITS

Chest exercises may be the most satisfying type of exercise to do, and they're capable of giving you the most spectacular results. Previous chest exercises concentrated on developing the muscles of the shoulders and the triceps, both of which play a role in the pectoral exercises. Now that these have been strengthened and conditioned, you're in a position to make real progress in developing the pectoral muscles. For men, a strong, well-defined pectoral line is the basis for a masculine look to the upper torso.

For women it is equally important. Most women know that they can't increase breast size by weight training or any exercise. But they may not be aware that they can increase the measurement of the bustline — sometimes dramatically — by strengthening the pectoral muscles which lie beneath the breasts. Chest exercises also help eliminate sagging breasts by firming up those muscles underneath the breast tissue. These exercises are particularly worthwhile for young women who enjoy the braless look.

PUSH-UPS

Don't ignore the Push-Up because it's a familiar exercise. It really works the chest, triceps, and shoulders, and can be done anywhere without special equipment.

There are a number of variations including the regular Push-Ups, "Women's" Push-Ups, Between-Chair Push-Ups, and "Resistance" Push-Ups. If you can't manage 15 regular Push-Ups when you start out, do as many as you can and then finish the set with Women's Push-Ups. If you can only do one or two of the regular Push-Ups, that's a good start. However, in each succeeding workout, try to work toward a goal of 15 regular Push-Ups.

REGULAR PUSH-UPS

Position

Lie face down on the floor, palms about shoulder-width apart, fingers pointing straight ahead. Push yourself up off the floor, straightening your arms and keeping your back and legs straight.

The Exercise

1. From the starting position, lower yourself until your chest just touches the floor (don't let your knees touch or your full weight rest on the floor).

2. Push yourself up again, legs and back straight throughout the exercise. Once down and back up again constitutes one complete repetition.

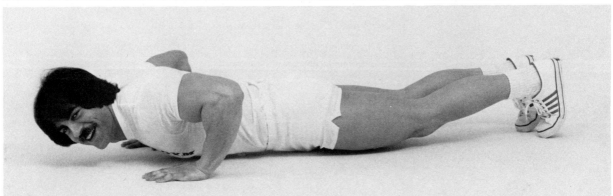

"WOMEN'S" PUSH-UPS

This variation of regular Push-Ups is designed for people who lack the upper-body strength to do regular Push-Ups. Since women are rarely encouraged to develop much strength in that part of the body, this is the kind they are most often taught. It's a good starting exercise for some men as well. Whether man or woman, after you have done it for a while, the exercise will be too easy and you'll want to move on to other push-up exercises in this section.

Position

Lie face down on the floor, palms about shoulder-width apart, fingers pointing straight ahead. Keeping your back straight and your knees on the floor, straighten your arms and push yourself up off the floor.

The Exercise

1. Lower yourself until your chest just touches the floor (don't let your full weight rest on the floor).
2. Push yourself up again, knees on the floor and back straight. (By pivoting from the knees instead of the toes as you normally would, you have a lot less weight to lift and the exercise is made much easier.) Once down and back up again constitutes one complete repetition.

BETWEEN-CHAIR PUSH-UPS

This variation is more strenuous than regular Push-Ups and comes closest to the workout you'd get with the Bench Press.

Position

Set two chairs a little farther apart than shoulder-width. Make sure they won't slide out from under you when you put your weight on them. Get in the Push-Up position with your palms on the seat of the chairs, your toes on the floor.

The Exercise

1. Lower your upper torso between the chairs as far as you can. The farther you lower yourself, the more strenuous the exercise.
2. Push yourself back up, keeping your legs and back straight. Once down and back up again constitutes one complete repetition.

Tip

You can make this exercise a bit more strenuous by putting your feet up on a third chair while you do your Push-Ups between the other two.

Caution

Always make sure that the chairs you are using are secure — it takes almost no time at all to go from staring at the floor to suddenly finding yourself on it.

"RESISTANCE" PUSH-UPS

If you really want to increase the resistance when you do any kind of Push-Ups, have another person put his or her hand on your back and gently push down. It doesn't take much extra resistance on their part to make a lot of difference. This variation gives Push-Ups a progressive resistance component so that your 15 Push-Ups will always work your body hard enough to give you the full benefit.

DUMBBELL PRESS

This exercise, which thickens the pectoral muscles, is most beneficial if done while lying on a bench so your elbows can drop lower than your body and really stretch the pectoral muscles. If you don't have a regular weight-training bench available, it's possible to do it on the floor, but we recommend using some sort of support like a piano bench or a couple of chairs pushed together.

Position

Lie on your back holding a dumbbell above each shoulder, arms fully extended. Bring the weights together so that their ends just touch and the palms of your hands are facing toward your feet.

The Exercise

1. Slowly lower the dumbbells straight down beside your shoulders in a kind of reverse Push-Up movement (if you aren't using a bench, your elbows will touch the floor).
2. As you lower the weights, rotate them so that the palms of your hands face one another.
3. When you can lower the weights no further, lift them back up until your arms are straight and rotate them back to the starting position.

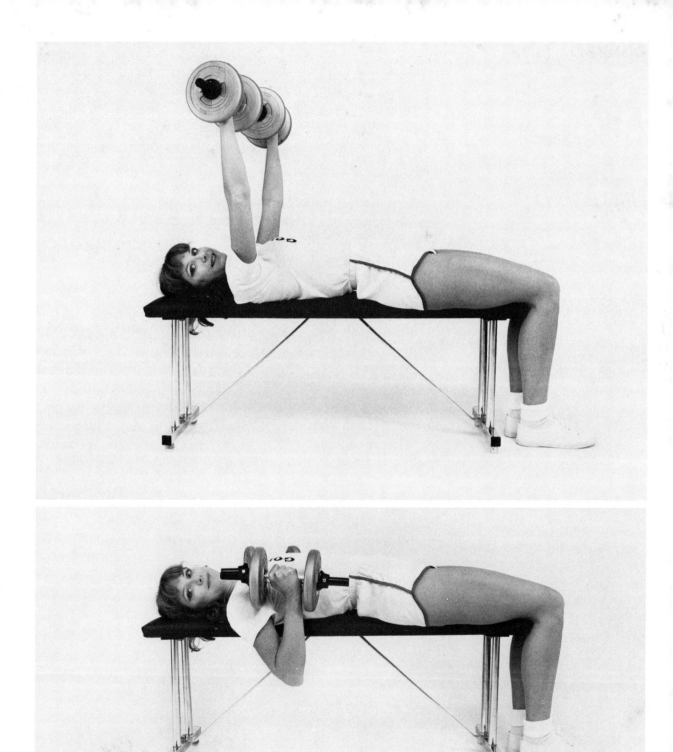

109

DUMBBELL FLYS

This exercise works the upper chest, stretches the pectoral muscles and expands the ribcage. For women, it's an important exercise for maintaining a high bustline. An art collector recently paid several hundred dollars for a rare photograph of Marilyn Monroe doing Dumbbell Flys. Apparently she understood the importance of weight training for maintaining her figure.

Position

This is another exercise that works better if you do it on a bench. Lie on your back holding a dumbbell above each shoulder, nearly over your face. Arms should be fully extended. Turn your hands so that your palms face one another, keeping the dumbbells about a foot apart.

The Exercise

1. With your arms nearly straight, slowly lower the weights in an arc to each side as far as they can go. The lower you get them, the more you'll stretch and shape the pectoral muscles. If you aren't using a bench, don't let the weights touch the floor.
2. When you've reached the lowest point, bring the weights slowly up again, *squeezing* the chest muscles together as you lift. This maintains tension on the pectorals. When you get back to the top, the weights should be about a foot apart.

Caution

Don't rotate the dumbbells as you lower them — keep them parallel to one another since this puts the right kind of stress on the chest.

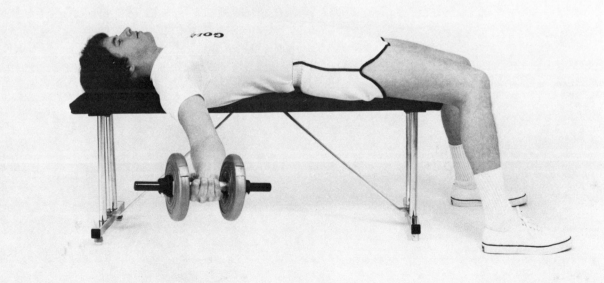

BENCH PRESS

Bench Presses are one of the finest all-around upper-body exercises, working not only the pectoral muscles but the shoulders and triceps as well.

Position

If you have a Bench Press bench you can just lie down, reach up and lift the bar off the supports. If you don't have that kind of bench, you'll need someone to stand over you and carefully hand you the bar.

Lie on your back, your hands holding the barbell with your arms extended straight up in the air above your chest, your grip a little wider apart than shoulder-width. Your palms should be facing your feet. Some people try to put the bar across their lap, lie down and then move it up to their chest where they can lift it into position. This is a waste of time: if the bar is light enough for you to succeed in that maneuver, you might as well stick to Push-Ups.

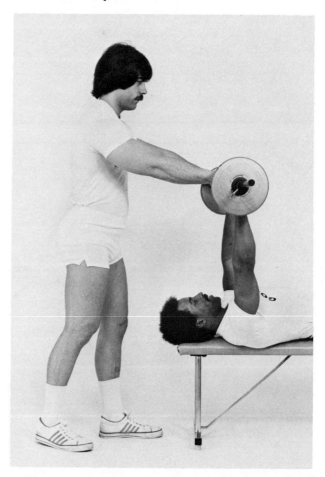

The Exercise

1. From your arms-extended position, lower the bar so that it touches your chest.
2. Raise it up again until you're back in the starting position. Make sure you keep the lifted bar over your chest; don't let it slide down toward your stomach.

Tip

With your hands just a little wider than your shoulders, you should have plenty of lifting power. The farther apart your hands are on the bar, and the harder it is to lift the bar, the more this exercise directly affects the chest.

Caution

Even when you are using a bench and don't need a partner, it is still a good idea to have someone standing by. That way you can go ahead and "rep out," do enough repetitions to exhaust the muscles, without fearing you might get too tired to get the bar up off your chest.

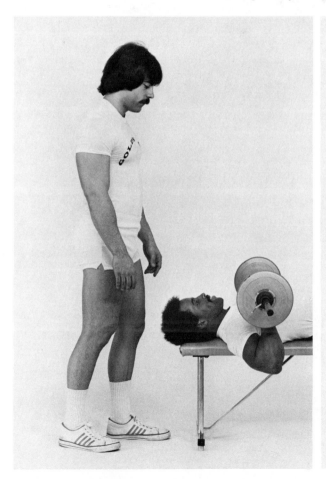 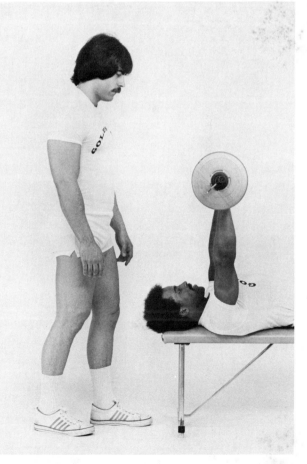

Incline Presses and Decline Presses are simply Bench Presses done at an angle instead of on a flat bench. Inclines are done with the shoulders higher than the hips, Declines with the hips higher than the shoulders. The different angles change the type of stress you put on the muscles.

In the Incline Press you press the weight at an upward angle and this works the upper part of the chest. When you do Decline Presses you're pressing down toward your lower body

and this works the lower pectoral muscles. You'll find you can't lift the same amount of weight at the three angles: you'll lift the least amount doing Inclines, a bit more with Bench Presses, and the most doing Declines.

You can use an adjustable bench to do Dumbbell Presses and Flys at these other angles, too. The change in angle has the same effect on these exercises as it does on Bench Presses.

PULLOVERS

Pullovers work the chest and the lats, expand the ribcage and help to condition the abs — they're a fantastic conditioning exercise for both men and women. You can do Pullovers either with one dumbbell or a barbell.

DUMBBELL PULLOVERS

Position

Lie across a bench at a 90 degree angle, your shoulders on the bench, your head hanging unsupported. Keep your feet flat on the floor, your pelvis lower than the bench. Take the dumbbell in both hands and hold it straight up over your head. One end of the dumbbell should be pointing toward your head.

The Exercise

1. Keeping your arms fully extended, lower the weight toward the floor as far down behind your head as you can. Keep your pelvis low, since this makes you stretch more.
2. When you have the dumbbell as low as you can, bring it back up to the starting position in a wide arc, arms as straight as possible. As you do this, concentrate on pulling with the pectoral muscles rather than with the arms.

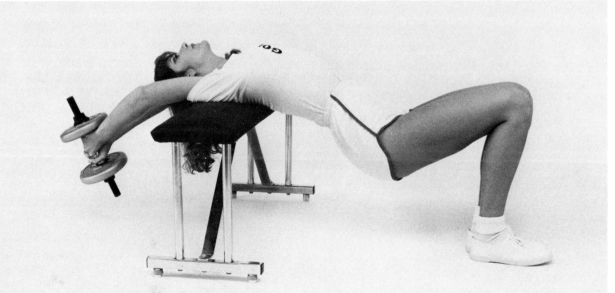

117

BARBELL PULLOVERS

Some people prefer doing Pullovers with a barbell. Your body is positioned differently across the bench, and you can't stretch quite as far, but you might find it a little more comfortable. Try them both to see which you prefer. If you like, you can use them alternately in your workouts.

Position

Lie on your back on the bench, your head just off the end of the bench. With an overhand grip, hold the barbell at arm's length above you, hands a little less than shoulder-width apart.

The Exercise

1. Keeping your arms as straight as possible, lower the bar toward the floor as far down behind your head as you can.
2. When you've got it as low as possible, bring it back up in a wide arc, keeping your arms straight. Concentrate on pulling with the muscles of the chest.

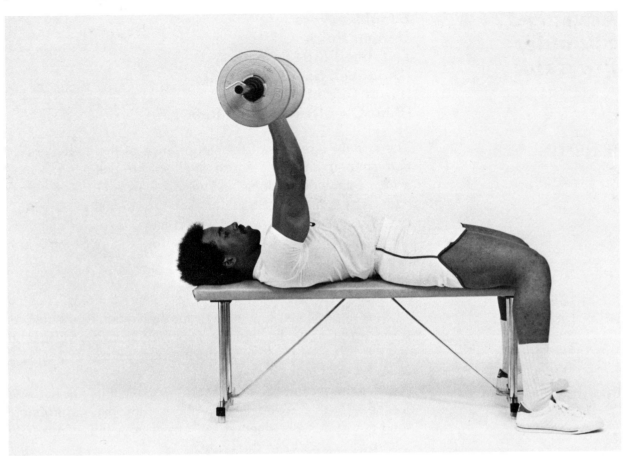

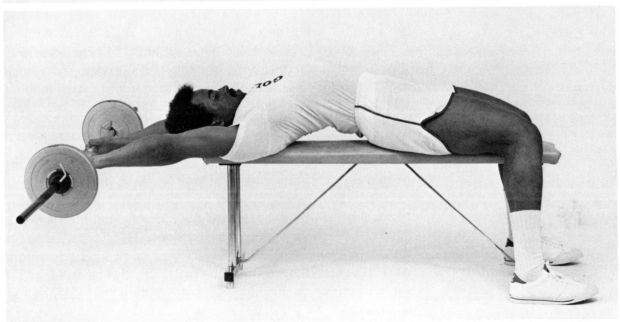

119

Advanced Shoulder Program

Shoulder Press
Upright Rows
Dumbbell Side Laterals
[Dumbbell Shoulder Press]
[Front Dumbbell Raise]
[Bent-Over Rear Deltoid Raise]

BENEFITS

There is no question of the importance of the shoulders for both strength and appearance. Well-shaped deltoids give men a broad-shouldered look and women a firm-looking upper body. The Advanced Shoulder Program strengthens the muscles you use when you carry or lift bags, boxes or children, and has a related beneficial effect on the neck and arm muscles.

DUMBBELL SIDE LATERALS

Dumbbell Side Laterals work the sides of the deltoids, creating a full, rounded look, equally as important when the shoulders are covered as when they are exposed; having well-shaped deltoids has a lot to do with making our clothes fit well.

Position

Stand with a dumbbell in each hand, palms facing one another. Bend forward just slightly so you can comfortably bring the dumbbells together in front of your hips, arms fully extended and close to the body.

The Exercise

1. Leading with the back of the hand, raise the dumbbells up and out to each side in a wide arc until they are just above your shoulders. As you lift, squeeze the muscles of the back together gently. Throughout the movement, the dumbbells should remain just slightly in front of the body, as they were when you started.
2. Pause for a moment at the top.
3. Slowly lower the dumbbells to the starting position, keeping them under control. Don't let them drop.

Caution

Make sure, on the way up and back down, that the palms of your hands are turned toward the floor. This keeps the stress on the side of the deltoids where you want it. If you rotate your hands so that the thumbs point up, the bicep takes up some of the stress, keeping you from getting the full benefit of the exercise.

DUMBBELL SHOULDER PRESS

The Dumbbell Shoulder Press works the deltoids (and, to some extent, the triceps) in much the same way as the Barbell Shoulder Press we learned in Level I. However, here the shoulders and arms are forced to work independently, making balance somewhat of a problem. The rotating movement further brings out the shape of the deltoids.

Position

You can do this exercise standing, sitting on a bench or in a chair. If you use a chair, it should have an upright back so that you sit straight up. Pick up a dumbbell in each hand and "clean" them (much as you would a barbell) to shoulder level. Turn your hands so that your palms face one another, elbows close to your side.

The Exercise

1. Simultaneously, raise the weights straight up overhead, rotating them slowly so that your palms face forward at the top of the movement, as though you were holding a barbell.
2. Lower the dumbbells simultaneously, rotating them back to the starting position.

Tip

There's a little trick seasoned weight trainers use to get heavy dumbbells up to shoulder level. Sit on a bench or in a chair and rest the dumbbells on your thighs. As you start to lift the weight up toward your shoulder, raise your leg quickly to give the dumbbell a little push. Do this first with one dumbbell, then the other.

You'll notice with this and other exercises that, as your arms get closer to being fully extended, it becomes easier to handle the weight. This is no illusion; you are stronger with your arms extended since this gives you a leverage advantage. One way to get maximum advantage from the Dumbbell Shoulder Press is to lift the weights until your arms are almost but not quite fully extended. By keeping your elbows slightly bent you increase the difficulty and get more from the exercise.

FRONT DUMBBELL RAISE

As the Side Lateral exercise works the side of the deltoid, the Front Dumbbell Raise shapes and develops the front of the deltoid.

Position

Stand with your arms hanging directly in front of you, a dumbbell in either hand. The palms of your hands should be facing toward your body.

The Exercise

1. Starting with either hand, lift the weight in an arc in front of you until it is just above the level of your head. At the top, the weight should be *directly* in line with your face rather than opposite your shoulder. Keep your arms as straight as possible throughout the movement.

2. Pause for a moment on top.

3. Slowly lower the weight to the starting position, your arm continuing to remain as straight as possible.

4. Repeat with the other dumbbell. Remember, whenever you are alternating dumbbells, do 15 repetitions with each of them, for a total of 30 repetitions.

Caution

When you lift the dumbbell, be sure to *lift* it — don't swing it up. If you find the weight is too heavy for you to lift without "cheating," use a lighter weight.

BENT-OVER REAR DELTOID RAISE

This exercise, which completes what you might call our "grand tour" of the shoulders, is a good example of how changing the angle of a movement can drastically alter its effect on the body. You've already learned movements for the front and the sides of the deltoids; the Bent-Over Deltoid Raise shapes and strengthens the back of the same muscle.

Position

Sit on the edge of a bench or chair and set the dumbbells down on the floor beside your feet. Bend over as far as you can, so that your torso is nearly parallel to the floor. Take hold of the dumbbells and bring them together underneath your thighs, your arms fully extended, palms of the hands facing one another.

The Exercise

1. Keeping your body bent over and your palms turned toward the floor, raise the weights in an arc to both sides and slightly forward until they are higher than your head. As you lift the dumbbells, squeeze the muscles of the back together gently.

2. Pause for a moment on top and then slowly lower the weights to the starting position.

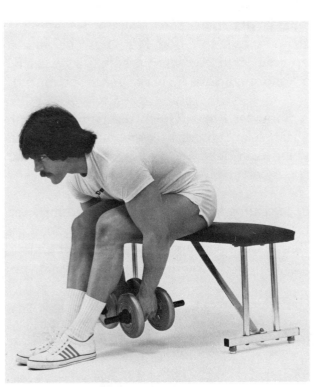

Advanced Back Program

Bent-Over Rows
Deadlifts
Good Mornings
[Chins]
[Straight-Legged Deadlifts]
[One-Arm Dumbbell Rows]

BENEFITS

The Back Program is designed to help men and women develop better posture. Good posture will not only make you *look* taller and leaner, it will actually make you taller.

But there's more to the Back Program than that. Our modern, sedentary lifestyle frequently results in the occurrence of lower back pains. The weight of our upper body compresses the spine and it's up to the muscles of the lower back to struggle to keep us upright. This can lead to considerable discomfort if those muscles are not conditioned and strengthened. These exercises will help to eliminate that problem.

The Advanced Back Program further builds upper-body power which is needed in sports like tennis and golf.

GOOD MORNINGS

Good Mornings help to reduce the waistline as they condition the lower back muscles (the lower back, after all, is part of the waist). The exercise is called "Good Mornings" because it resembles a deep bow, as if you were greeting a respected acquaintance (in a more gracious time and place, of course).

Position

Start by doing a Shoulder Press. Grasp the barbell with an overhand grip, clean it and press it over your head. Then lower it down behind your head and neck and rest it on your shoulders, keeping it balanced with your hands.

The Exercise

1. Keeping your legs *straight*, bend forward from the waist until your torso is almost parallel with the floor, and your back arched slightly. Keep your head up and look straight ahead.
2. Pause for a moment and raise to the starting position.

Caution

We said to keep your legs straight. Any time you do this, you put additional strain on your back. Be extra careful not to use too much weight.

CHINS

Chins work the lats and are one of the most basic and beneficial exercises you can do for your back and shoulders.

This is a very difficult exercise for some people so don't be discouraged if, at first, you can't do even one full rep. That's normal — you'll make progress quickly as you get used to the exercise. In the beginning, it doesn't matter how high you actually lift yourself. Even if you just kind of "twitch" — pull up toward the bar with little discernible progress — you will still be strengthening the muscles involved.

Position

If you are using a portable chinning bar, fasten it securely in a doorway. Stand underneath and grasp it with your palms turned away from you. Curl your legs up and hang from the bar.

The Exercise

1. Pull yourself up from the fully-extended position until your chin is level with the bar.
2. Lower yourself back down to the starting position and relax so that you can feel yourself fully extended again.

Tip

The farther apart your hands are, the harder the exercise. At first, you are probably going to need to keep them fairly close. As you get stronger, position them as far apart as you can.

A partner can be a great help by holding you around the waist and lifting as you do Chins. With that little extra help you'll be able to do quite a few reps with full movement right from the start.

STRAIGHT-LEGGED DEADLIFTS

This is an exercise for the lower back in which you lift with your upper body as if doing a deadlift but keep your legs straight so that you concentrate the effort on the back. Without your legs to help you lift, you're going to have to use a lot less weight. It is particularly important when you do a movement that puts stress on your lower back that you not use more weight than you're sure you can handle. If you experience *any* discomfort in your back while doing it, use a lighter weight or go on to something else. Your back will get used to heavier weights in time.

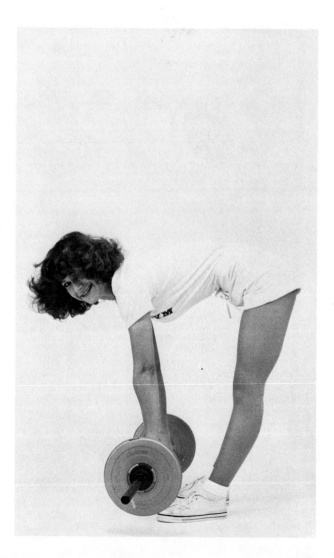

Position

Grasp the bar with a Deadlift grip, one hand overhand, the other underhand, about shoulder-width apart. Straighten your legs so that the weight comes up off the floor, but keep your body bent over, the weight hanging down, arms fully extended.

The Exercise

1. Keeping your arms straight and the barbell hanging down in front of you, straighten up and stand in an upright position, pulling your shoulders back a little as if coming to attention.
2. Pause for a moment.
3. Bend forward again from the waist, keeping the legs straight, and lower the weight as far as you can toward the floor.

ONE-ARM DUMBBELL ROWS

This is an exercise that primarily works the lats, but it also involves the rear deltoids and — because of the twisting motion of the torso — the obliques and the lower back as well.

Position

You will alternately work the right and left side. Take hold of a dumbbell in your right hand and stand with your left foot slightly ahead of the right. Bend forward until your torso is approximately parallel to the floor. With your left hand hold onto a table, chair or some other support for balance, or put your elbow across your left knee. Let your right shoulder, arm and the weight hang straight down beneath you toward the floor.

The Exercise

1. Still in the bent-over position, lift the weight upward to your chest by raising your shoulder and rotating your torso. Your elbow should point directly at the ceiling. (Don't bring the weight up to the chest by Curling with the bicep.)
2. Pause for a moment.
3. Lower the weight — your torso should rotate back the other way and you should end up with your shoulder, arm and the weight stretched toward the floor. Do 15 repetitions before switching to the other side.

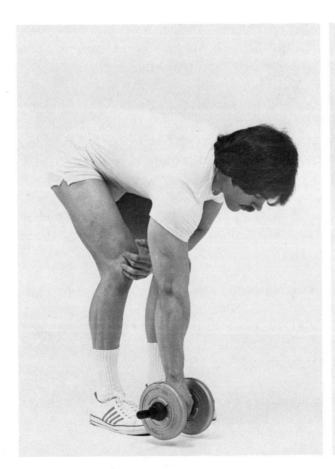

Advanced Arm Program

Barbell Curls
Tricep Curls
Wrist Curls
[Dumbbell Curls]
[Tricep Press]
[Reverse Wrist Curls]

BENEFITS

The arm program works your biceps, triceps, wrists, and forearms. These muscles are very important for most sports movements. Throwing, for example, is a shoulder and tricep movement, as is serving a tennis ball. The tricep area, which makes up two-thirds of the upper arm, is also one which tends to sag when we get older or don't get enough exercise.

Any sport that uses a club or racket or bat is helped by strengthening the forearm and wrist, because those muscles determine the strength of the grip. When it comes to shaping the forearm, it takes quite a while to see any results. But you can strengthen and firm them quickly. You may not have occasion to notice the change on the tennis court or golf course, but you will the next time you open a jar.

TRICEP CURLS

Almost every sport utilizes your tricep muscles. This is a good type of exercise to do after a squat or a deadlift because it works only one specific body area and gives you a breathing space between movements which require a complete bodily exertion.

Position

This exercise is done with one arm at a time. Take a dumbbell and lift it straight overhead, drawing your elbow close to your head.

The Exercise

1. Bend your elbow, lowering the weight slowly behind your head until it touches your back.
2. Keeping your elbow close to your head, straighten your arm, raising the dumbbell to the starting position. Do 15 repetitions, then switch arms and do 15 more.

Caution

A simple but very important warning: As you get tired be extra careful so that you don't bump yourself on the head with the weight.

WRIST CURLS

Anytime you use your hands, you rely on the strength of your forearms. Despite their name, that's the part of your arms that Wrist Curls work.

Position

Pick up the barbell with an underhand grip, hands slightly less than shoulder-width apart. Sit on a bench or in a low chair with your forearms resting on your knees, your hands and wrists unsupported, sticking out beyond your knees.

The Exercise

1. Bend your wrists back and lower the barbell toward the floor, letting it roll down toward the tips of your fingers.
2. When your wrists are fully bent, and the bar is held just by the tips of your fingers, reverse the process: roll the bar back into the palms of your hands, bringing your wrists up.
3. Keeping your forearms firmly on your knees, continue the upward movement with your wrists and curl the bar as high as it can go.

Caution

Do the exercise slowly so that the bar doesn't roll past your fingertips and drop to the floor.

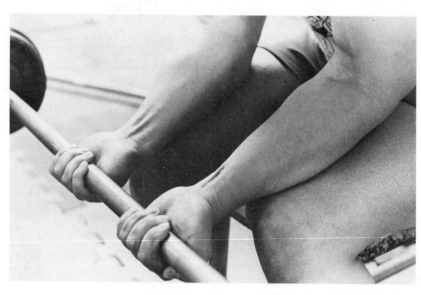

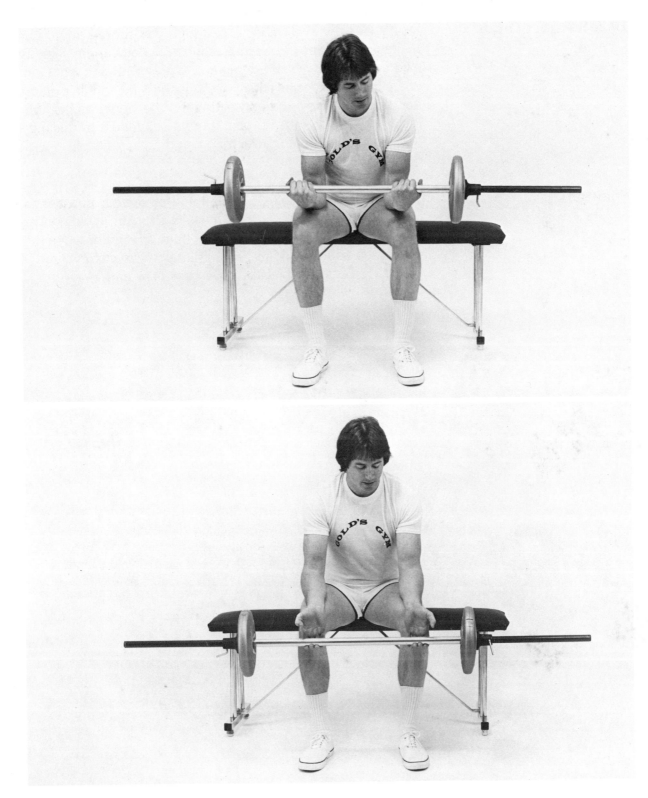

DUMBBELL CURLS

Doing Curls with dumbbells can give you more variety and make your routines more interesting than doing them with just a barbell. As we've said, doing an exercise with different kinds of weights changes its effect. A slight change in angle or manner of doing a movement can shape the upper rather than lower part of the muscle, give it more roundness or thickness and affect one part more than another in multiple-muscle groups.

Position

You can do Dumbbell Curls standing or seated on a bench. Either way make sure your back is straight. Holding one weight in each hand, let your arms hang straight down beside you. Keep your shoulders back, your elbows well forward and the palms of your hands pointed straight ahead.

The Exercise

1. Bending your arm at the elbow, lift one dumbbell forward and up, keeping your elbow anchored as a pivot.

2. As the weight gets to the top of the movement, give a little extra "cramping" movement to the bicep.

3. Lower the weight slowly, keeping it in full control. At the bottom, your arm should be fully extended so that the bicep is stretched as much as possible.

4. Alternate, doing 15 repetitions with each arm.

You can also do Dumbbell Curls with both arms simultaneously instead of one at a time.

Caution

As you Curl the dumbbell, don't let your hand rotate at all — that takes the stress *off* the bicep and you lose some benefit from the exercise.

TRICEP PRESS

This is a tricep exercise, designed to build strength and bring out the full shape of the muscles at the back of the upper arm. The Tricep Curls worked those muscles side to side; the Tricep Press works them with a barbell in a back-to-front motion.

There are various ways to do this exercise: standing or sitting, or lying down on a bench or the floor. You don't have to limit yourself to doing just one of these variations. Include Standing (or Sitting) Tricep Presses in one routine, Lying Tricep Presses in another. You might even include one variation in your first circuit and the other in the second. However, if you prefer one, there's no reason why you have to alternate.

STANDING TRICEP PRESS

Position

Although this is called the Standing Tricep Press, you can do it just as well sitting down. Grasp the barbell with an overhand grip, hands 4 to 6 inches apart, feet comfortably apart for balance. Clean the weight and press it over your head. Your hands should be closer together than they would be for a normal Shoulder Press.

The Exercise

1. Let the weight down slowly behind your head, keeping your elbows pointed up and your arms as close to your head as possible. When you've lowered the bar as far as you can, you will really feel the pull on your triceps.
2. Raise the bar again and return it to the starting position, your arms extended over your head.

Caution

You'll have to use much less weight with this exercise than you would for a Shoulder Press, or you risk dropping the bar behind you. Start out cautiously and find how much weight is right for you.

LYING
TRICEP PRESS

Position

This exercise is best done on a bench, although it's possible to do it lying on the floor. Lie on your back, holding the barbell at arm's length directly above your chest, hands about 4 to 6 inches apart. If you're using a bench, position yourself so that the top of your head is just over the end.

The Exercise

1. Keeping your elbows as close together as possible and your upper arms stationary so that your elbows act as a pivot, lower the weight over your head toward the floor.
2. If you're on the floor, let the weight down until it almost touches the floor. On the bench, continue to lower the bar as far as you can.
3. When you get to the lowest point of the movement, return to the starting position, with arms fully extended above you.

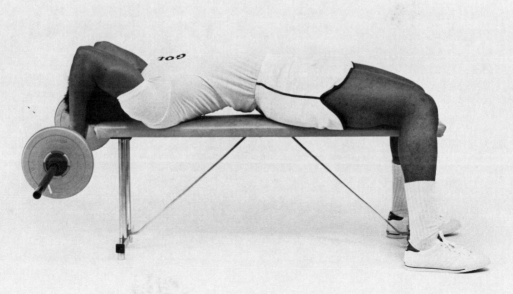

REVERSE WRIST CURLS

Reverse Wrist Curls are exactly what their name implies: the reverse of a Wrist Curl. Both exercises are designed to shape and strengthen the wrist and forearm. This one works the muscles you use to bend back your hand, the top side of the forearm.

Position

Sit in a chair or on a bench as you would for Wrist Curls, your forearms supported by your knees, your hands about 6 inches apart, extending over your knees — only this time hold the barbell with an *overhand grip*.

The Exercise

1. Leaving your forearms on your knees, bend your wrists forward and down, lowering the bar as far as you can.
2. At that point, lift the bar back up and bend your wrists back, raising the bar as high as it will go. Remember, do this movement with your wrists, not your arms.

Tip

We've been emphasizing that it's best to let your muscles rest between exercises and not to do two body-part exercises in succession if you can help it. Wrist Curls and Reverse Wrist Curls are an exception. Doing them one right after another gives you a tremendous pump.

Advanced Leg Program

Front Squats
Lunges
Seated Calf Raises
[Hack Squat]
[Leg Extensions/Curls]
[Standing Calf Raises]

BENEFITS

Shape the calves, streamline the knees, tighten the thighs — all of that can come from the Advanced Leg Program. And it will produce a tremendous effect on your performance in most sports.

Women particularly have a special interest in exercising their legs. Because of their hormones, extra fat on their bodies is deposited first on the hips and thighs (men pick it up around the middle). The best remedy is to minimize the fat by a careful diet and to firm and shape the lower body with the Advanced Leg Program.

One of the things for which Gold's Gym is famous is variety of equipment for exercising legs. Even though you won't have the same equipment at home, working on your own and with a partner on these exercises will help you achieve the same kind of results you would get if you trained at the Gym.

LUNGES

Lunges are good exercise for developing the long-legged look. They bring out the contours of the leg because they work both the quadricep (front of thigh) and hamstring (back of thigh) muscles. Balance may be difficult, so working in front of a mirror will help you maintain control.

Position

As you did to get ready for Good Mornings, pick up the bar with an overhand grip, clean it, press it over your head, then lower it behind your neck and rest it on your shoulders, keeping it balanced with your hands.

The Exercise

1. Stand upright with your feet together. Keeping your head up and your back straight, take a long step forward with one foot, bending both knees so that the knee of the trailing leg just brushes the floor.
2. From this position, push yourself back up and bring your feet together to the starting position. The trailing leg should remain stationary.

3. Repeat the same movement with the other leg. Alternate until you finish 15 reps with each leg.

Caution

As you step forward remember to keep your back straight: the weight should remain centered over your hips. If you bend forward you'll put extra strain on your lower back and that's not what this exercise is all about.

SEATED CALF RAISES

Well-shaped calves can add immeasurably to the attractiveness of the leg. Strong calves are absolutely essential for any quick movement in sports. A tennis, basketball or football player, a sprinter — anyone who has to get off the mark in a hurry — can benefit greatly from calf work.

As with ab exercises, there is no limit to the number of calf raises you can do. It makes more sense, though, to add more weight to the bar, and do fewer reps.

Position

Sit on a bench or chair and place a 2-inch thick telephone book (or something of about equal size) on the floor in front of you. Rest your toes on the book with your heels on the floor; you should feel the stretch in your calf muscles. Pick up the barbell and rest it across your knees. (Pad the bar with a towel for extra comfort.)

The Exercise

1. Raise up on the balls of your feet, lifting your heels as high as you can.
2. When you're as high as you can go, lower your heels to the floor again. If you don't feel the stretch in your calf muscles, try using an object that elevates your toes even more.

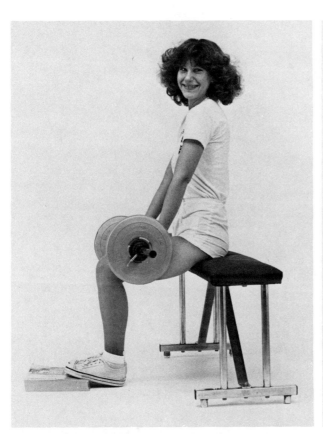

HACK SQUAT

This exercise works the thighs and the buttocks like a Squat without putting any strain on the back. One advantage it has is to tie the thigh muscles into the hip, giving you a long-legged look.

Position

With the barbell on the floor *behind* you, bend down and grip it so that your palms face behind you. Stand up. The barbell should be hanging just below your buttocks.

The Exercise

1. Without arching your back, bend your knees and lower your body as far as you can, keeping your heels on the ground.
2. Once down, push yourself up — but not all the way. Stop when you've gotten about three-quarters of the way up.
3. Pause in this three-quarters position and then do another repetition.

Tip

Not straightening your legs completely keeps the maximum stress on them and increases the value of the movement. Concentrate on keeping your balance.

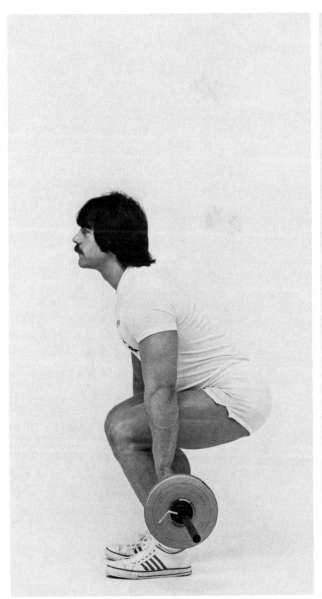

LEG EXTENSIONS / CURLS

Leg Extensions shape and define the quadriceps, the thigh muscles — and Leg Curls work the biceps, the back of the leg. Normally, the Gold's Gym machines are used to do these exercises but at home you can get help from a weight training partner.

LEG EXTENSIONS

Position

Sit on the edge of a table, cabinet or chair that is high enough to allow your legs to swing freely. Hold on the edge to give yourself stability. Have your partner kneel or squat in front of you, hands on your ankles.

The Exercise

1. Lift your legs straight ahead against the resistance of your partner's hands. The resistance should be just enough to make the movement difficult but not impossible.

2. When your legs are parallel to the floor, pause.

3. Resist while your partner pushes them back down to the starting position.

You can also do Leg Extensions with one leg at a time. Do one repetition of each leg, alternating until you have done a total of 30 repetitions.

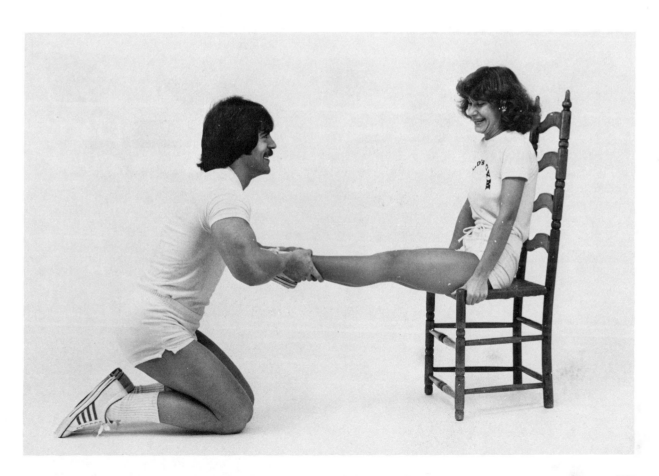

LEG CURLS

Position

Lie on your stomach on the bench, your knees just to or beyond the end. Have your partner grip your ankles.

The Exercise

1. While your partner applies resistance to your ankles, lift them and bring them as close as possible to your buttocks.
2. When you've pulled up your ankles as close to your body as you can, pause.
3. Resist as your partner pulls them back down to the starting position.

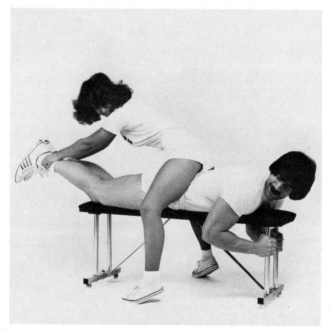 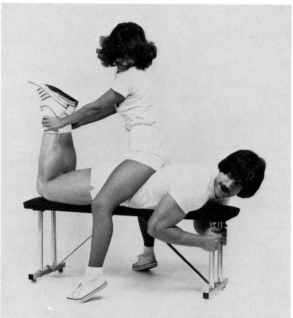

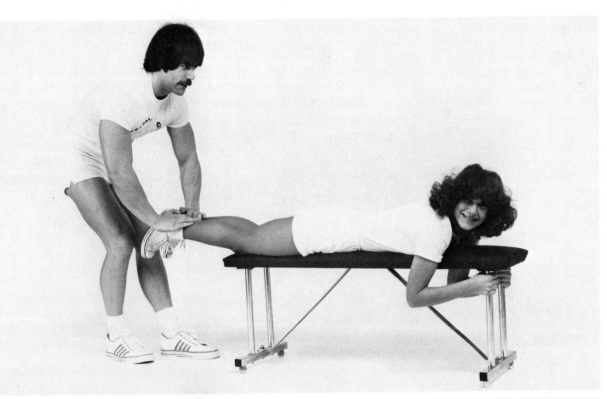

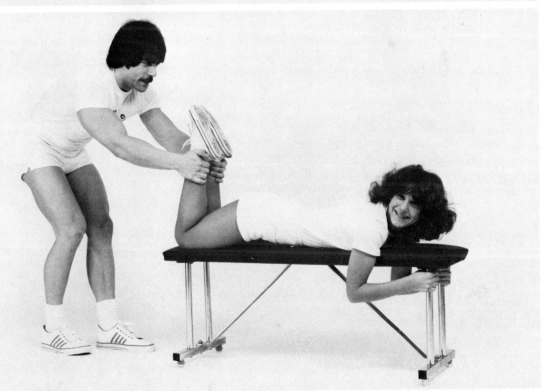

Variations

You can do Leg Extensions and Curls by yourself using a dumbbell between your feet, as shown.

For those times when your partner isn't available, you can do Extensions and Curls as isometric exercises. For Extensions, sit close to a wall, put one foot up against the wall and try to extend the leg. Push as hard as you can for six seconds, then relax. Do this two or three times. To do Curls, stand, turn your back to the wall, put your foot up against it, and try to curl it up using the wall as resistance.

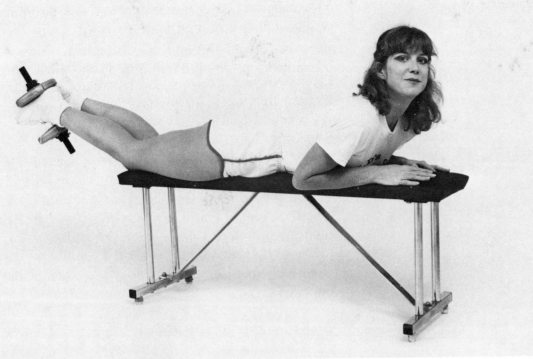

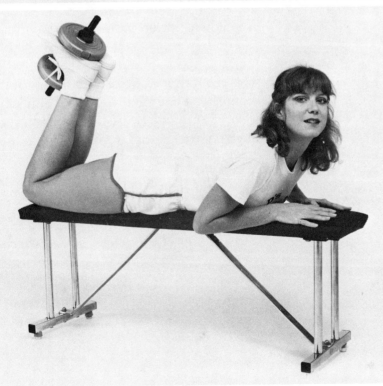

STANDING CALF RAISES

Seated Calf Raises work the soleus muscle on the lower part of the calf. Standing Calf Raises, on the other hand, work the upper part of the calf and give it a full, broad shape. As you get stronger with this exercise, use a higher riser — lifting your toes further off the floor — and do the movement with more weight. Until you get used to balancing or unless you have a partner standing behind you to keep you steady, you can do the exercise with no weight at all.

Position

You can use either a barbell or dumbbell for this exercise. If you use a barbell, grasp it with an overhand-underhand grip as you would for a Deadlift, pick it up and hold it at arm's length in front of you. If you use dumbbells, pick them up and hold them at your sides.

Place the balls of your feet on a telephone book, block of wood or something similar, your heels remaining flat on the floor.

The Exercise

1. Keeping your legs straight, raise your heels as high as you can.
2. At this point, pause.
3. Slowly lower yourself down until your heels return to the floor.

Tip

This is another exercise, like those for the wrists and forearms, where it's beneficial to do two similar movements in succession. Try doing Seated and Standing Calf Raises one right after another to get a maximum "pump" to your calves.

Waist Program

Leg Raises
Crunches
Bent-Legged Sit-Ups
Twists

BENEFITS

When you follow the Waist Program and develop your abdominal muscles, you'll see a surprising reversal of that "middle-aged sag" that many of us tend to get long before middle-age. Winning the Battle of the Bulge starts with a proper diet because no matter how firm and trim your underlying muscles may be, nobody's going to see (and appreciate) them if they're covered with a layer of fat. But a good program of abdominal exercise coupled with proper diet can lead to extremely satisfying results.

If you've ever tried to serve a tennis ball or just throw anything with pulled ab muscles you know how important they are to generating power in many physical movements. In addition, the condition of your abdominal muscles greatly affects some of your internal organs. When your abs stretch and sag, it can adversely affect your health.

The abdominal muscles are the most under-used muscles in the body. Because of this we recommend you include all four exercises in the Waist Program in *every single exercise session*. While the abs are muscles and need to be exercised, they are the one group of muscles that shouldn't be trained with long exercise movements. Abs are best exercised with short, hard, "cramping" movements.

CRUNCHES

The Leg Raises you've already learned in Level I work the lower abdominal area while Crunches, a kind of cramped sit-up, develop the upper abs. Try to do at least 25 Crunches, more if you can. One of the ways to increase your number of repetitions is to relax for just a few seconds after 10 or 15, then do 10 or 15 more.

Position

Lie on your back, resting your feet against a wall, a piece of heavy furniture, or a partner. Your feet should be several feet above the floor, and your knees slightly bent. You might want to put a thin pillow under the small of your back.

The Exercise

1. With your hands behind your neck, try to bring your head toward your knees as if you were doing a Sit-Up. You'll find, in that position, that all you can manage is a kind of cramping movement. That's a Crunch.

2. You can increase the effort directed at your abdominal muscles by pushing with your feet, lifting your pelvis slightly and turning your knees upward a bit as you come forward with your upper body.

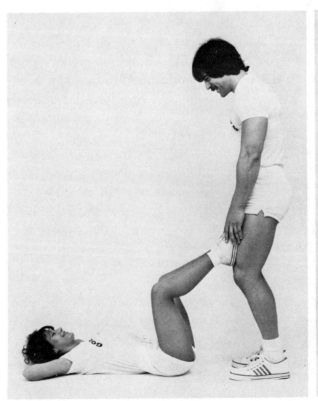 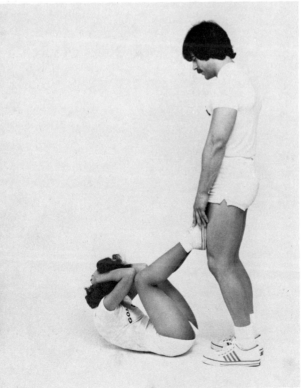

BENT-LEGGED SIT-UPS

Most of us were taught to do Sit-Ups with our legs straight. But doing them that way is inefficient — it puts strain on the back and makes the thighs work along with the abs. Doing Sit-Ups with your legs bent concentrates the effort on your abs.

Again, try to do at least 25 reps, and more if you can. Add one extra repetition each workout session until you are doing all you can "stomach." Do them in increments of 10 or 15, resting for just a few seconds between sets.

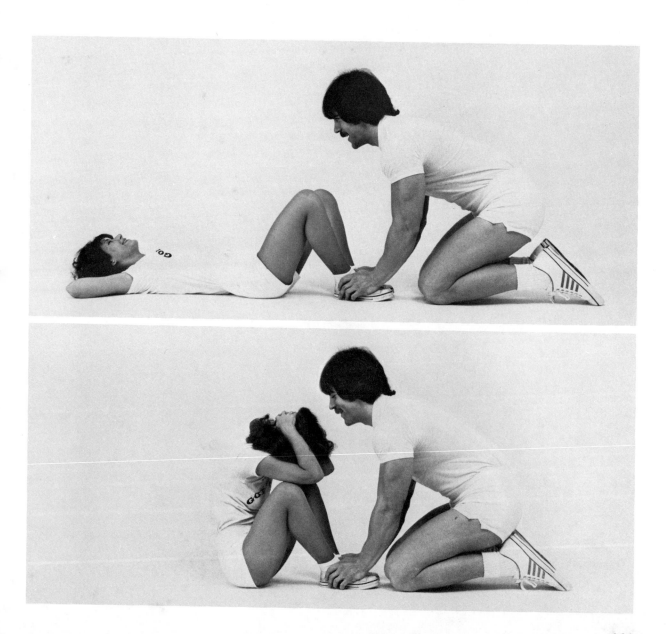

Position

Lie on your back, hands behind your head and knees bent. Hook your feet under a piece of furniture or a weighted barbell — or have a workout partner hold onto your ankles.

The Exercise

1. Sit up and try to touch your head to your knees.
2. When you are as far forward as possible, give a little extra "cramp" to the ab muscles, as if doing a Crunch.
3. Lower yourself down, making sure you stay completely under control — don't flop. That way you keep your ab muscles working throughout the entire exercise.

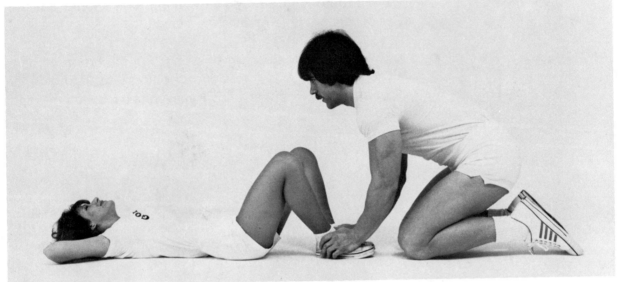

TWISTS

Twists work the external oblique muscles that run down either side of the lower torso — that area where we tend to develop "love handles," those bulges at the upper hips and waist. The obliques are involved with twisting and turning your body, hence the name of the exercise.

To do Twists you're going to need one additional piece of equipment: a broom or mop handle, hopefully with the broom or mop no longer attached. Don't use anything heavy like the bar from your weight set.

Start by doing 25 reps (in *each* direction) and try to work up to 100. There is no limit to how many you should do; the more repetitions, the greater the benefit.

Position

You can do Twists standing or sitting. Put the broom handle behind your neck and across your shoulders, taking hold of it a few inches from either end. Keep your back straight, and

eyes directly ahead. If you're standing, keep your feet wide enough apart to keep your hips from turning. If you're sitting, keep your knees apart for balance. This exercise is done in one continuous movement.

The Exercise

1. With pelvis immobile, twist your shoulders and torso as far as they can go to the right.
2. Without pausing, return to the forward position, then twist your shoulders and torso as far as possible to the left.
3. Return to forward position.

Caution

Be careful to turn, not "swing." You want your muscles, not momentum, to move you. Keep your head forward at all times. Another checkpoint: keep your shoulders and the broom handle level — don't dip as you turn. This keeps everything lined up perfectly.

Weights and Sports

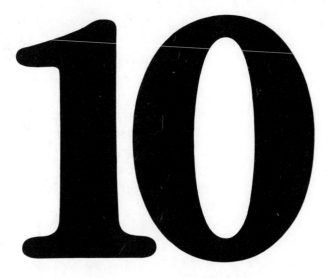

10

BEYOND FITNESS

Sports require both general fitness and special strengths for individual activities — quick reflexes for tennis, upper-body coordination for golf, supple legs and torso for skiing. Some weight programs isolate the muscles needed for a specific sport and make them the exclusive focus of development. But the Gold's Gym weight-training program combines whole body conditioning with routines tailored to the individual sports preference.

The circuit training particularly helps with cardiovascular endurance and will allow you to play for longer periods without becoming winded and stressing your heart.

This chapter keys the exercises to the requirements of selected popular sports — for full- or part-time athletes who want to fine tune their bodies to a favorite game.

THE WEEKEND ATHLETE

You may have time for sports only on weekends, but you can stay in condition all week with 15 minutes a day and the Gold's Gym program. Then when you get out to the tennis court, golf course, or softball field, your skills may be a little rusty, but your body will be ready to give its best. You'll get more enjoyment and have greater success in those weekly sport sessions, and you won't have to pay for it with a painful Monday morning. Your general conditioning will minimize the risk of pulled muscles and the other ills that often befall otherwise sedentary people who overexert themselves on weekends.

But there's much more to weight training than just holding

your own. Coaches and athletes all over the country use it extensively to improve performance. You can, too, by adapting the program to the sport you like to play.

Excellence in sports involves constant practice. The key to a perfect pitch or a well-placed serve is concentrated repetition of the movement. Weight training can help by keeping your body responsive to commands for specific actions. You start with the basic all-body circuit, but then comes the bonus: you add specific exercises to develop the abilities and special strengths you require in your particular sport.

HOW THE BODY WORKS IN SPORTS

Each part of the body makes a specific contribution to sports activity. If you look closely at the three basic body areas—legs, torso and upper body—you'll see that there are a number of fundamental movements each of them can perform, and a corresponding series of training exercises. You can design a series of additional weight-training exercises to improve your performance in any sport.

Legs

Your legs are the foundation of almost every sport skill and, as most athletes know, the first to show signs of fatigue and lack of conditioning. There are three basic things you call upon your legs to do:

Push

This is a movement in which you drive forward with power, the way a football lineman does when he takes on a blocker. It is also how you generate power for stroking a tennis ball, swinging a golf club, or pitching and hitting a baseball. To develop this kind of strength the basic exercises are: **Squats, Leg Presses, Calf Raises.**

Jump

For this power move, used by high jumpers, broad jumpers and basketball players, you train the same way you would for pushing moves, but you add: **Squat Jumps.**

Do squat jumps either with no weight at all or with a light barbell across the back of your shoulders. Squat down, as in regular squats, but then, instead of just standing up, push up quickly and jump into the air as high as you can.

Quick starts and stops

Some sports require the ability to start and stop in a hurry; others, such as tennis, basketball or soccer require quick, lateral moves. To develop these skills, add to your routine: **Leg Extensions / Curls, Lunges, Calf Raises.**

Torso

The torso — abdomen, external obliques, lower back — generates its own power, and is also instrumental in transmitting power generated by the legs to the upper body to help you make use of your total strength. Your torso performs the following movements:

Twist

You use the twisting movement whenever you swing, throw an object, or shot put. The basic exercises which help you to do this are: **Twists, One-Arm Dumbbell Rows.**

Anything to do with the torso is improved by strong abs, so you need your full complement of: **Ab Exercises.**

Crunch

This is a movement in which you use your ab muscles to pull your upper body down and forward, as when you're serving in tennis or pitching a baseball. For this movement you need: **Sit-Ups, Crunches, Leg Raises.**

Lift

Whenever you stand upright from a bent-over position, or lift something in front of you, you engage the muscles of the lower back. In order to strengthen them (and this is a problem area for some people) you should do: **Deadlifts, Straight-Leg Deadlifts, Good Mornings.**

Upper Body

The upper body consists of the chest, shoulders, arms and upper back. Upper-body strength is important to many sports movements, but usually the other parts of the body come very much into play as well. Can you imagine a shot-putter trying to do his thing sitting on a stool? Or a pitcher trying to strike out a batter from a kneeling position? The primary movements of the upper body are:

Push

If you push something that's straight ahead of you the shoulders, chest and triceps are what you use. A number of exercises can help you with this, including: **Bench Presses, Push-Ups, Dumbbell Presses, Tricep Extensions/ Curls.**

Your shoulders are important in pushing, too, especially if you're pushing something up and over your head. For this movement you would train with the tricep exercises and add: **Barbell/Dumbbell Shoulder Presses.**

Pull

This is the opposite movement to the push and uses mostly the back and biceps. You would use this movement when rowing, participating in a tug-of-war or performing certain swimming strokes. Important exercises are: **Chins, Bent-Over Rows, One-Arm Dumbbell Rows, Barbell/Dumbbell Curls.**

Lift

Lifting, a power move in sports like basketball and football, is also involved in bowling, underhand throwing, and some ten-

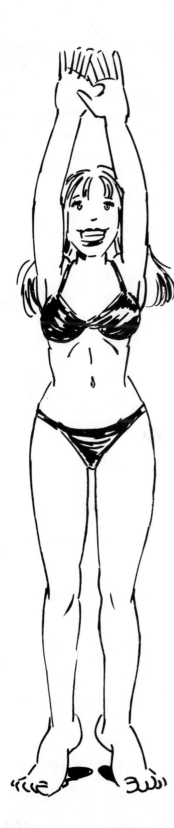

nis shots. Lifting something in front of you always involves the lower back. In addition, you work the biceps so you need to exercise with: **Barbell/Dumbbell Curls.**

The shoulders are also involved and you should train these with the: **Front Dumbbell Raise.**

If you are lifting to the sides, as in a golf swing or tennis back-hand, add: **Dumbbell Side Laterals, Bent-Over Deltoid Raises.**

Throw

We're using this as a general description for all of the overhead movements which involve "deltoid rotation," that is, the kind of rotating movement the shoulder goes through when you throw a ball. You use the same motion in tennis serves, certain kinds of basketball shots and many swimming strokes. For the shoulders you should do: **Pullovers.**

For the arms: **Tricep Extensions/Curls.**

The crunching movement of the torso is important, so include: **Ab Exercises.**

Rotate

This is the basic motion you use to hit a baseball, perform a tennis forehand, pitch sidearm and throw a discus. Power is generated in the legs, usually by a stride or a shifting of weight, transmitted through the torso by a twisting motion, and ampli-fied by the arms, back and shoulders. Once you've worked on *your leg and torso exercises you should add:* **Chins, One-Arm Dumbbell Rows, Bent-Over Rows** for the lats.

For the arms: **Curls, Tricep Extensions/Curls.**

To strengthen the shoulders: **Dumbbell Side Laterals.**

And for the chest: **Flys.**

DESIGNING YOUR OWN TRAINING PROGRAM

Think about how you use your body in certain sports, and what movements and movement-sequences are most important for your performance. Then you'll begin to see how weight training exercises can benefit you. Here are some suggested exercises, sport by sport, which are now being used by professionals and top-ranked amateurs to improve their game.

As you are planning your personal sports training program, it's important to remember that the entire body is involved in any kind of strenuous athletic activity. For maximum results, particular training exercises should always be integrated into an overall body conditioning program.

In Chapter 9 we showed you how to design a personal body-shaping program around the skeleton of the basic Level I and Level II circuits. Specific exercises were added to each day's training routine to emphasize different body parts. To train for individual sports, you do pretty much the same thing, utilizing the appropriate exercises for your sport. For example, let's say that you are a tennis player and analyze the weaknesses in you game as being:

1. You're too slow getting to the net;
2. You have trouble stopping and changing direction quickly;
3. Your serve is weak;
4. You can't get enough pace on your backhand.

Based on this analysis you decide that the particular exercises you need to emphasize are:

1. Calf Raises, Squats and **Leg Curls** for quicker starts;
2. Lunges and **Leg Extensions** to help stop and change direction;
3. Pullovers, Shoulder Presses and **Tricep Presses,** coupled with extra **Abdominal** work for your serve;
4. Front Dumbbell Raises, Side Laterals, Wrist Curls and **Reverse Wrist Curls** for your backhand.

Once you have selected the important exercises to help you with your sport, there are basically two ways to integrate them into your overall training program.

**Include your special exercises
in your daily body part routine**

As you continue to work a different body part each day, make sure to include in your selection of body-part exercises the ones you have determined will be helpful to your sports performance. Thus, when it came time to work legs, you would be sure to emphasize **Calf Raises, Squats, Leg Curls, Lunges** and **Leg Extensions** while continuing to train the rest of the body by doing the basic circuit exercises. Likewise, when doing a Shoulder Program, you would be certain to include **Front Dumbbell Raises, Dumbbell Side Laterals** and **Shoulder Presses** in your routine.

**Design a special sports training routine
to include in your program one day a week**

This is a good method if you're striving for extra progress and development in a given area. It should only be done once a week because, as we've stressed, athletic performance puts a demand on the *entire* body and if any areas are ignored, that performance will ultimately suffer. However, one day a week can be set aside for attacking particular problems with special programs. Using the same tennis example we can come up with a one-day program which looks like this:

Circuit I	**Circuit II**
Squats	Lunges
Pullovers	Dumbbell Side Laterals
Leg Curls	Leg Extensions
Front Dumbbell Raises	Tricep Presses
Wrist Curls	Reverse Wrist Curls
Sit-Ups	Crunches
Leg Raises	Twists
Seated Calf Raises	Standing Calf Raises

As you can see, these circuits include all of the exercises our analysis has determined will help particular weaknesses in a tennis game.

Tennis and Other Racquet Sports

To play tennis well, it is extremely important to be able to start and stop quickly. The exercises that help you do this are **Lunges** and **Calf Raises**.

You generate power for the swing by the strength of your legs and a twisting motion of your torso. The exercises are **Squats** and **Twists.**

The shoulder, arm, and hand are your connection to the racquet. The exercises are **Side Laterals, Front Dumbbell Raises** for the shoulders, **Curls** and **Tricep Presses** for the arms, and **Wrist Curls** for the wrists and forearms.

Incidentally, it's better to do these exercises for both sides of the body, even though you primarily use only one. Symmetry is an aspect of beauty and also seems to help the body's coordination.

To improve your tennis serve, you are going to need Ab Exercises. The abdominal muscles have a lot to do with the power you are able to generate when bringing the racket over your head. A combination of exercises will help you with that. Start with a **Pullover**

and as you get the bar up to your chest, lift it up in a **Bench Press.**

Golf

Golf demands a different movement from the body than does tennis. Only recently have golfers come to realize how much being in shape can improve their game, especially under the pressures of tournament competition. Although golf doesn't involve the running and cardiovascular demand of tennis, the golf stroke, like the tennis swing, is generated from the legs and a torso twist. For these movements, do **Squats** and **Twists.**

Any shoulder, arm or wrist exercise can be of benefit to the golf swing, especially **Side Laterals, Tricep Presses, Wrist Curls.**

You will also put a lot more power in your swing with **Ab**

Exercises. Incidentally, doing a few twists with a club across your shoulders instead of a broom stick is a very good way of helping you warm up on the first tee, or if you've had to wait a long time between shots.

Skiing

Any kind of upper-body work can benefit a skier who must constantly twist and turn the upper body and maneuver the ski poles. But the greatest stress will be put on the legs. So do a lot of **Squats** and **Lunges.**

You can do more sets than you normally would as you get ready for a skiing weekend, or you can try to do more than 15 reps. After all, on the slopes, you will be bent over and flexing your legs for hours at a time.

To help prepare your body for the bent-over skiing position, do a lot of **Ab Exercises, Lower Back Exercises, Stiff-Legged Deadlifts.** Handling the poles will be helped by **Pullovers, Side Laterals, Tricep Exercises, Wrist Curls.**

Bowling

The stride and foot movement essential for good bowling scores can be helped by **Lunges.**

The lifting motion of the torso can be strengthened by **Lower Back Exercises.**

To improve shoulder movement, use **Front Deltoid Raises.**

Your connection to the ball are the bicep, forearm and wrist, so concentrate on **Curls, Wrist Curls.**

Swimming

The best way to train your legs for the kicking motion is with **Leg Extenstions, Curls**.

Your torso plays an important part, too. You get power from a crunching movement of your abs, much like you do·in a tennis serve, and you constantly have to twist and arch your back. To train for this do **Ab** and **Lower Back Exercises**.

Reaching out and pulling the water toward you with your arms involves a kind of rowing motion which works the lats. You're best prepared for that movement by **Bent-Over Rowing, Chins, One-Arm Dumbbell Rows**.

Shoulder strength is vital to swimming and you should do as many shoulder movements as you can, concentrating especially on **Deltoid Rotation Movements**

and add to this some chest work like **Flys** and **Pullovers**.

TEAM AND INDIVIDUAL SPORTS

Because athletes playing different positions on a team are called upon to carry out different kinds of activities, training techniques can vary greatly even in a single sport. The level of strength and overall conditioning required by most team sports — and gymnastics, wrestling, and track and field — is far greater than most of us who participate in sports just for fun would care to achieve. However, since coaches are more often than not encouraging their athletes to try weight training, here are a few that are being used extensively in training programs.

Football	Lower Body	Torso	Upper Body
	Deadlifts	Ab/Lower Back	Shoulder Pressses
	Squats/	Exercises	Pullovers
	Squat Jumps		Curls
	Leg Extensions/		Tricep Presses
	Curls		Bench Presses/
	Calf Raises		Push-Ups
			Bent-Over Rows
			Wrist Curls
Gymnastics	**Lower Body**	**Torso**	**Upper Body**
	Deadlifts	Ab Program	Shoulder Presses
	Squat Jumps		Curls
	Lunges		Tricep Presses/
			Curls
			Pullovers
			Wrist Curls
Basketball	**Lower Body**	**Torso**	**Upper Body**
	Deadlifts	Ab Program	Shoulder Presses
	Squats		Curls
	Squat Jumps		Tricep Presses/
	Leg Extensions/		Curls
	Curls		Pullovers
	Lunges		Bench Presses/
	Calf Raises		Push-Ups
			Chins
			Wrist Curls
Baseball	**Lower Body**	**Torso**	**Upper Body**
	Squats	Ab Program	Shoulder Presses
	Squat Jumps		Tricep Presses/
	Leg Extensions/		Curls
	Curls		Pullovers
	Lunges		Side Laterals
	Calf Raises		Bench Presses
			Wrist Curls

Volleyball

Lower Body
Squats
Squat Jumps
Calf Raises
Deadlifts

Torso
Ab Program

Upper Body
Shoulder Presses
Tricep Presses/
  Curls
Curls
Bench Presses
Wrist Curls
Pullovers

Bicycle Riding

Lower Body
Squats
Lunges
Leg Curls
Calf Raises

Torso
Sit-Ups
Leg Raises
Crunches

Upper Body
—various
movements
for general
conditioning

Soccer

Lower Body
Squats
Squat Jumps
Leg Extensions/
  Curls
Deadlifts
Lunges
Calf Raises

Torso
Ab Program

Upper Body
Shoulder Presses
Bench Presses
Tricep Presses/
  Curls
Wrist Curls

Index

Bill Dobbins

A radio, television, and magazine writer in Los Angeles, Bill also writes screenplays and music. Several years ago he started training at Gold's Gym, where he acquired an interest in all forms of physical fitness.

Ken Sprague

The owner of Gold's Gym, Ken is widely acknowledged as one of the world's leading experts in weight training. A high school and college track star whose interest in physical fitness brought him to weight training eighteen years ago, he is a former Mr. Cincinnati and finalist in the Mr. America contest. He is secretary of the National Amateur Athletic Union and promoter for the Mr. America contest for the AAU as well as for many local and regional body building contests across the country.